W9-BNA-407

caught in the crossfire

caught in the crossfire

growing up in a war zone

Maria Ousseimi

Walker and Company New York

To my parents

First published in the United States of America in 1995 by
Walker Publishing Company, Inc.

Published simultaneously in Canada by Thomas Allen & Son Canada,
Limited, Markham, Ontario

Library of Congress Cataloging-in-Publication Data
Ousseimi, Maria.
Caught in the crossfire : growing up in a war zone / Maria
Ousseimi.
p.   cm.
Includes bibliographical references and index.
Summary: Uses incidents from Lebanon, El Salvador, Mozambique,
Bosnia-Herzegovina, and Washington, D.C., to examine the effect on
children of growing up in a war zone.
ISBN 0-8027-8363-5. — ISBN 0-8027-8364-3 (pbk.)
1. Children and war—Juvenile literature.   2. Children and war—
Pictorial works—Juvenile literature.   [1. War.]   I. Title.
HQ784.W3097   1995
305.23—dc20   94-44457
CIP
AC

Book design by Maryann Leffingwell

Printed in the United States of America

2   4   6   8   10   9   7   5   3   1

Photography credits are as follows: pages viii, 4, 8, 9, 16, 18 (top), 19, 20–21, 24, 33, 34, 36, 37, 39, 41, 45, 46, 47, 95, 102,
103, 104, 106, 107, 108, 109, 111, 115, and 116–117 by Sueraya Shaheen; pages 3, 5, 7, 18, (bottom), 48, 51, 53, 54, 57,
59, 60, 62, 63, 64–65, 66, and 68 by Marwan Tarraf; pages 76 (bottom left and bottom right), 80, 81, 82, 83, 84, 87, 89,
and 91 by Ziad Moukheiber; pages 92, 99, 112–113, and 114 by Dion Johnson; pages 96–97, 100, and 118 by Lloyd Wolff;
page 15 by Maria Ousseimi; page 12 courtesy of the Lebanese Red Cross; page 89 by Lucian Perkins; page 90 by Steve
Snieder; page 100 by Heather Courtney; pages 50 and 69 courtesy of former United Nations High Commissioner for
Refugees, C. Sattleberger; pages 28–29 and 30 provided by Magnum. Photographs on the following pages provided by
Reuters/Bettman: ii, 70, 74–75, 76 (top), 79, and 85 by Corinne Dufka; 26 and 44 by Nancy McGirr; 32 by Javier Bauluz;
72 by Charles Miller. Photographs on the following pages provided by UPI/Bettman: v and 42 by Ivan Montecinos; 35 by
Oscar Sabetta.

contents

acknowledgments

My special gratitude to Richard Wormser, whose writing skills helped bring the children's stories to life. My warmest thanks to Lamia Abu-Haidar, whose assistance and research were invaluable to me. Her interviews of children in the former Yugoslavia brought very powerful stories home, and her constant support was much appreciated. I wish also to thank the following people for their support and encouragement: In New York: my editor, Emily Easton, for sticking with me despite my unorthodox methods, and Jill Bertuccio at Applied Graphics Technology. In Mozambique: Michele de Rossay, Jean-Victor N'kolo, and Armedia. In El Salvador: Rolando Lopez, Daniel Santos Dimas, Jose Luis Enrique, Lizie Panameno, Rafael-Horacio Magana della Torre, and Mario Cader. In the former Yugoslavia: Anita Jakovec. In Washington, D.C.: Ras Omar Kush, Dewey Reeves, and Cynthia at New Community and After School, an advocacy program; Jimmy Carter at Martha's Table; Steve Snyder; the Latin American Youth Center; and Jimila. In Lebanon: Middle-East Airlines, Nagib Choueri from Kodak Near East, and Jad Akhawi.

I would also like to thank the photographers for dedicating their time and talent to this project: **Marwan Tarraf,** who is working as a cameraman at Reuters, Beirut. His photographs have appeared in several international publications. **Sueraya Shaheen,** who earned a B.F.A. in Photography at the Corcoran School of Art while working on this project. **Ziad Moukheiber,** who is currently completing his master's degree in Interactive Telecommunications at New York University. **Dion Johnson,** seventeen years old and formerly homeless, is a graduate from the Shooting Back Photography program in Washington, D.C., and is currently a part of the "Streets to Skills" program. His work has been shown at Smith Howard galleries and has appeared in various local and national magazines. Many of Dion's achievements are due to his friend and mentor of five years, **Lloyd Wolff,** an award-winning photographer and teacher living in Washington, D.C.

Finally, my deepest appreciation to everyone I interviewed.

author's note

I am one of the lucky ones. My family was able to leave Lebanon at the beginning of its seventeen-year-long civil war. But I have always been haunted by those I left behind—friends, schoolmates, neighbors. How have their lives been shaped by their violent childhoods? And how would my own perception of the world have changed if I had stayed behind? Would I even have survived?

I needed to find answers to these questions, to connect with the often forgotten victims of that war and the other wars being broadcast into my comfortable living room night after night. I had to walk through the bombed-out streets of Beirut, my former home, to look into the eyes of children who had lost everything, to let them know someone cares.

And just going back to Lebanon wasn't enough. I felt compelled to travel to as many different continents as I could to show people that war is not confined to a particular region or a particular culture. It's easy to distance ourselves from the horrible truths of war by thinking of it as something that only happens far away, to someone else. But many American children grow up in war zones of a different kind. I wanted to reveal the violence of Washington, D.C., a city many look upon as a symbol of peace and prosperity but which, shockingly, is one of the most dangerous cities in the nation.

Even though the topic of children and war is a hard one and this book may be a little harsh at times, it is important to hear the children's stories, to stand witness to their suffering. Their voices have been silenced for far too long.

1

childhood lost
lebanon

The sky was bright blue and clear on this July day in 1972. On the ground, tens of thousands of people had gathered to celebrate the arrival of the Concorde—the world's fastest commercial airplane. It was due to land in Beirut, Lebanon, for the first time in the country's history.

The supersonic boom of the Concorde signaled its arrival. The crowd cheered and danced as the graceful, eaglelike plane floated to earth like a feather and gently touched down on the runway. To the Lebanese people, it seemed a happy omen of their future had descended from the sky.

On the surface, Lebanon seemed like a Garden of Eden. It was blessed with mountains and seashores, a mild climate, rich farmland and orchards, and beautiful cities. The country was small enough that one could ski in the mountains in the morning and swim at the seashore in the afternoon. The city of Beirut was a jewel, filled with movie theaters, stages, bars, restaurants, and clubs. It offered six universities for the nation's population of only 4 million people. Students from all around the world came to study at the American University of Beirut, the best in the Middle East. The Lebanese people had a long history, even though the country of Lebanon had existed only since 1948, when it was created by an agreement between Britain and France. The Phoenicians, an ancient maritime people, had prospered here thousands of years earlier.

But beneath Lebanon's surface was a "fault line." And a social earth-

Beirut before the war.

quake was about to erupt. The country was divided between Muslims and Christians, haves and have-nots. Over 100,000 Arab refugees had fled from Israel (once Palestine) and settled in Lebanon since 1948, threatening the delicate balance that existed between Christians and Muslims. Geographically, Lebanon was right in the middle of the conflict between its southern neighbor, Israel, and its northern neighbor, Syria. The south of Lebanon, on the border with northern Israel, has rarely known peace since the creation of the State of Israel in 1948. From 1967 onward the Palestinians attacked Israel from the villages of the south, and Lebanese civilians fell victim to the retaliatory fire of the Israelis. In 1978 Israel invaded part of south Lebanon, an area now known as the security zone, to try to create a buffer between the Palestinian guerrillas, and Israeli territory. In 1982, the Israeli army, in the operation "Peace for Galilee," invaded Beirut to strike the final blow against the Palestinian movement. It invaded Lebanon from the south, leaving a trail of death behind.

A few months after the arrival of the Concorde, Israeli warplanes roared through the night sky and attacked the Palestinian refugee camps of Beirut in an attempt to stop the guerrilla attacks on Israel launched by Palestinians from Lebanese soil. The raids were a prelude to a war that was soon to erupt.

On April 13, 1975, Palestinian guerrillas attempted to assassinate a Christian right-wing leader, killing his bodyguard instead. In retaliation, Christians blew up a bus carrying Palestinian students. This spark ignited a conflict that lasted fifteen years, from 1975 to 1990. Beirut was suddenly divided into two sections, East and West. East Beirut was controlled by right-wing Christians who wanted the Palestinians disarmed or ousted. West Beirut was controlled by Palestinians whose ultimate goal was to defeat Israel and return to their homeland.

Beirut was transformed into a major battleground. Schools were closed; public offices were shut down. Gunfire and shelling roared day and night. Electricity was cut off. Checkpoints appeared on both sides of the city, and armed men took to the street. War also raged in the mountains and other rural regions. Many villages were invaded and their populations were either massacred or forced to flee. Gunmen ruled, and the people watched in horror as their country was destroyed and their homes and lives were ruined. Thousands of people poured into the city of Beirut—but there was no safety.

Rubble becomes a playground.

The war radically changed the lives of Beirut's children. Schools were closed for weeks at a time. The children were confined to their homes, so they could no longer go outside to play. They could not even call their friends, because the telephone lines were down. They seldom watched television, because there were only a few hours of electricity a day. When the shelling became intense, families would seek refuge in a bomb shelter. Sometimes, the shelter was no more than a cellar, a garage, or an underground room. When the shelling began everyone would rush downstairs, taking only their most precious belongings, such as money and important documents. Most shelters contained only the bare necessities: first-aid kits, fire extinguishers, water, canned food, and sometimes mattresses. Zeina, who is eighteen years old now, spent the early years of the war in shelters.

The shelter is horrible. It feels as if you are buried alive. You don't know what is happening outside. All you do is hear the shelling getting closer and closer. If your apartment had been destroyed, or if something had happened to your friends, you couldn't find out until you were out. Plus everyone is always on edge in shelters. People cry, scream, get angry at each other.

Living with armies seems normal *(facing page)*.

A common sight.

When there was a break in the fighting, people dashed outside to get food, candles, and whatever else they needed. Most children quickly got used to the shelling. But they seldom got used to the tiny shelters. They always felt the need to go out to run, play, and be in the sun.

To twelve-year-old Ahmad, a Muslim child who lived in West Beirut, the shelter was like a prison. Ahmad was born during the war; his mother was killed in the fighting. His father abandoned him. For Ahmad, the only place where he could have fun was in school.

Children usually do not like school because they feel confined there. But during the war everyone missed being in school, because they would rather be there than in the shelter where there is nothing to do. At school, they can see their friends, and play and talk about things.

Thirteen-year-old Mohammed was one of the children who refused to go to a shelter. As a result, he was seriously wounded. He lost a leg and suffered a serious head wound when a shell hit his house eight years ago. One of his sisters was killed, and his other brothers and sisters were badly hurt. After seventeen operations, Mohammed's condition is still guarded.

I hated staying in the shelter, and I was not scared of shelling. When there was shelling, everyone hid and I stayed in my room. I was sure nothing was going to happen to me anymore, that I knew the war.

As the war continued, children became military experts. They could tell from the sound of a shell how close it would land, how big it was, and how much damage it caused. They would say, "That was an 82mm-wide rocket," or, "This one's a 120," or "That was really strong, probably a 155." The war became their universe. Even their games changed. Children did not play hide-and-seek anymore. They invented games that reflected the war around them, like dodging snipers. Since almost every neighborhood had snipers who would shoot down civilians, adults and children alike, simply crossing a street was dangerous. Children began taking dangerous risks, running across the street despite sniper fire. They would think, "He has already fired three times. This time he won't do it." Sometimes these calculations would work. Sometimes they wouldn't.

One consequence of the war was that parents lost control of their children. They were under enormous pressure to protect and provide for them. But children became restless and would not remain confined at

Child playing with one of the shells that destroyed his home *(facing page)*.

home. For them the war had become commonplace, and the trick was to be able to avoid being killed while leading what they considered a normal life. Their views differed dramatically from their parents'. Having to worry about survival on a daily basis, they saw no point in planning for the future. Doing well at school or thinking about a career became pointless. Life had to be lived one day at a time. Having become unconcerned about danger, children disobeyed their parents and did as they pleased.

Before the fighting broke out, most Lebanese children lived together in peace. Christians and Muslims attended the same schools, and anyone could travel within the country freely. Once the war began, people had to stay in their own neighborhoods. It was very dangerous to cross over the Green Line, which divided the city. Many children could not see their friends any longer. Suddenly they were separated from people they cared about, for reasons they couldn't understand. Lina is a Christian teenager who had many Muslim friends before the war started.

Living in a no-man's-land *(facing page)*.

The journey home.

I had many school friends that I stopped seeing when the war began. I don't know what happened to them. In the beginning it was difficult to accept that we had become enemies. But at the end, what could we do, it was war. It was as if my friends lived in another country, when in reality they were just a few miles away.

Children became refugees as the fighting intensified; Jihan, fifteen, recalls the agony of fleeing.

After my father died, we fled from our village. They were massacring everybody, so we had to go. We went from village to village. It was not safe. The shelling was terrible. We arrived in Beirut and had to sleep on the streets. It was the most horrible time of my life.

While the majority of people were trying to peacefully adapt to war, some chose to get involved in the actual fighting as a means of survival. Children were either recruited as soldiers by organized militias or felt that fighting was the only option they had if they wanted to survive. For most of these children, involvement in the fighting was a way to obtain control over, and even conquer, death. Until the beginning of the hostilities, like many children around the world they had been playing war games. Now, they were players in a real war. Elie, now twenty-one, started fighting in the ranks of a Christian militia at fourteen. He was one of many teenagers who were fascinated by the gun culture that resulted from the war.

It was exciting in the beginning; you know how it is when you are young. You start carrying guns and think you are grown up. You get involved in situations that are much bigger than yourself. You feel you are more than a soldier. You feel like the police, or like a secret agent. The power gets to you, and you feel really grown up.

When Elie was sixteen, reality set in. He killed someone in a face-to-face encounter for the first time.

We were in the mountains and I saw him on the other side of the front line. He called to me and asked me to have coffee with him. There was no fighting and I was curious. I walked up to him and when I was thirty feet away, he pulled a gun on me. I had a gun in my back pocket. I pulled out the gun and shot him. I don't know why, but he wanted to kill me. When he fell to the ground, it really got me. He was the first person I killed up close. On the way back, I thought about his family. War is rotten. War destroys everything.

During the war, young boys carrying machine guns, arrested and terrorized people. Sometimes they killed them. The soldiers' power was unlimited. There were no laws. Might made right. Even though some young soldiers realized that what they were doing was wrong, they were not able to stop. The peer pressure was too strong, and the power was too enticing. Whoever carried a gun made the rules. Young fighters did not have to earn a living. They did not have to pay for their food and were given what they wanted. They went into stores and took what they liked. No one dared to refuse them anything.

A snapshot from his scrapbook shows Elie during his military training in the north of Lebanon.

Red Cross rescuers.

While many young men were taking part in the fighting, some others chose to serve in the helping forces of their country. The dangers were just as great. Jad, now thirty, served in the Lebanese Red Cross at age fourteen.

> *I lived just across the street from the Red Cross offices. Every day, I would see the ambulances leaving, and I would see everyone working. So I decided to go check it out. My parents were not thrilled, but you know parents did not control their kids anymore. It became very addictive. Time after time, we wanted to go on more dangerous missions. We felt nothing could happen to us. Now that I think about it, I can't believe I ever took such crazy risks. We would go into the most dangerous situations to get the injured. It became like a battle with death.*

Like experienced soldiers, members of relief teams also became fatalistic. They began to feel nothing would happen to them. Wassef, now 30, remembers his feelings.

The only time I remember being really scared was when one of my coworkers died. We were all stunned—it was like a reality check; we suddenly realized that we were not invincible.

For most teenagers who took an active part in the war, the glamour eventually wore off. Albert, Elie's younger brother, also loved to fight. Whenever there was a battle, he would rush to where the action was. "I used to love war," he says, "but in the end, I found myself with nothing." What helped change his mind was the death of one of his brothers. Albert was at an outpost when a shell hit a tank two miles away. His brother was inside. The loss, and his closeness to it, changed his attitude toward war.

There are many different kinds of losses in war. Waad's loss was physical. A teenager who lives in the south of Lebanon, she had volunteered to go to her aunt's house to borrow a kitchen item when suddenly there was an explosion.

I found myself on the ground. I heard people screaming. I heard some young men say 'get the car.' They put me in the car. I knew I had lost both my legs. All that was left was some flesh hanging down . . . I lost almost all my blood.

Elie's personal photo shows his brother Albert, at eleven, undergoing military training.

An Israeli shell had exploded near her. Waad, who is a Shiite Muslim, believes "it was God's will that this should happen to me." She says that she is not bitter, that the past is behind her; she still has her family, she points out. Yet, when she is asked her thoughts about soldiers, a sadly troubled look crosses her face, like a dark cloud crossing the sky. "They kill and kill," she says, and then falls silent.

Katia lost all the male members of her family when she was sixteen. She remembers how the enemy came to her village and made them lie on the ground. Then there was firing; all through the day, her brother and uncle lay calling for help. But no one could go to them. It was too dangerous. At last the wounded men fell silent and died.

> *People say to me I should forget it and put it all behind me. I try. I want to finish school. I want to help my family. But I still have nightmares. I will be reading and suddenly there it is. I long for the past, before this happened. There was the shelling, but at least we were with our family.*

Pascale, sixteen and Christian, is one of the many children who have little hope. She, too, lost all her male relatives in a massacre when army forces entered her village on the outskirts of Beirut and killed all the men they found. Pascale speaks of her spiritual loss:

> *War destroys the soul. You lose all hope. The war has ended but nothing has changed. How can we think about a future after all we have lived through?*

Whether they chose to fight, help, or just survive, all Lebanese children were affected by the war. Their view of the world and the future was irreversibly changed. Today many programs are attempting to teach Lebanese children to live in peace. UNICEF (the United Nations Children's Fund) is trying, through the "Education for Peace" pilot program, to teach them to trust in a brighter future and to become full participants in the future of their country. UNICEF organizes summer camps where children from different religious backgrounds meet and learn to live together. A volunteer staff of trained youngsters helps them overcome their war experiences through games and discussions. There are also programs in the different neighborhoods of Beirut where kids can go and spend time after school and on weekends.

"It was God's will that this should happen to me" (*facing page*). —Waad

But for most Lebanese, even though the war days are over, the suffering continues. Their city's destroyed buildings remind them of the horrors of the past. The downtown area of Beirut, even though totally destroyed, continued to shelter refugees long after the fighting ended. Those who were displaced, forced to leave their homes, are uncertain about their future. Some villages are still deserted. Some people continue to live in cars on the sides of roads as they have no place else to go. Others still live in bombed-out buildings and abandoned apartments, waiting to return to their former homes. Such shelters lack windows, running water, electricity, and heat.

Families with nowhere to stay are forced to live in their cars while waiting to return home.

Some people have been given new apartments; Jihan, for instance, lives with her mother and brother in a house donated by a charity organization. It consists of one small room containing three beds and a television. There is no bathroom or kitchen. Still, Jihan is grateful.

All we have left from our old life is our color TV. Still, I feel blessed to be living in this room. I know it is not much but it is better than nothing. Sometimes I remember our former house and it makes me cry.

When children are displaced they are not only forced to leave their homes, they are also uprooted from their communities. Families and communities create a buffer between the war and children. In extremely close communities, everyone's priority is the protection of its children from the outside world. When war succeeds in destroying families and uprooting entire villages, children lose their support systems. Jihan still feels insecure.

Ever since we were displaced, I feel completely lost. When I was younger I trusted adults. Now, after seeing what my elders have done, I don't trust anyone anymore.

In Lebanon today some children are still living with the constant threat of displacement. Waad has already had to flee several times from Zibqin, a very small village on the border with Israeli-occupied southern Lebanon.

What future do we have? I don't even know what is going to happen to us. We moved so many times. It is as if every time something happens in the world we get affected by it. All we want is to live in peace.

In order to survive, children who fled their homes and were forced to work at a very young age sacrificed their childhood to war. It will take many years for the wounds to heal and for people to realize that they can live in peace. Much effort will be needed to teach Lebanon's youth that there is an alternative to war and violence. These young people are the ones who will have to make sure that what happened in the past is not repeated in the future. In the middle of their destroyed city, the children of Beirut are slowly learning to believe in a brighter future.

The Lebanese civil war in Lebanon ended in 1989. (Although in Israeli-occupied southern Lebanon war is still raging between the Lebanese resistance and the Israeli army.) Unlike many civil wars, the one in Lebanon was not aimed directly at civilians and was fought mainly between militias. But the civilian population often found itself caught in the middle. During the seventeen years of war, several hundred thousand people

Working for a living *(top)*.

Little girl and her injured mother fleeing their village after it was shelled.

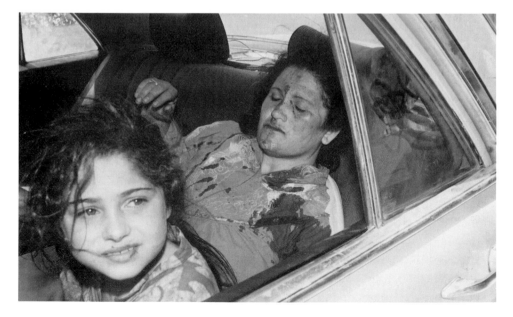

were killed, as many were crippled and injured, and more than half the population was displaced. As usual children paid the highest price. Forty-five thousand died as a result of the fighting, and many others were deprived of their basic needs for food, water, housing, and a stable environment in which to grow into responsible adults. Waad longs for the security that comes with peace:

Waad playing on the floor with her sisters, leaving her artificial legs on a couch in the house.

> *I would like to leave this country. I would like to live somewhere where nobody would get hurt. I wouldn't leave without my family. When the shelling starts, I hate it when everybody is not at home. I want my whole family around me when there is danger. I feel they can protect me.*

After seventeen years, Lebanese children do not like to speak of war. They have had enough. They are tired of hatred and violence. George is trying desperately to get his life back to normal.

Selling the past.

It is as if I was dead all those years. Today, the war is like a distant memory. Like a horrible nightmare. It is too crazy to face and understand. I was lucky to survive. I have to go on living and make something out of my life.

Unlike George, Zeina is pessimistic about the future.

Every time there is some political instability, I get worried that everything is going to start all over again. I can't think about building my future, because I don't trust the future.

Not all young people are glad the war has ended. Some young fighters who were accustomed to being feared and respected have now become normal citizens. It is very hard for them to accept their new status. They have lost their points of reference and have a very difficult time finding a role to play in a peaceful Lebanon. Having glorified violence, and not having learned another way to resolve conflicts, they have a hard time adjusting to a peaceful life.

To many young men, war was exciting. Samir felt "war was beautiful. At least to those who are fighting." He was unhappy when the fighting finally stopped.

All the young men in my neighborhood are angry because the fighting is over. War is something we got used to. The sound of gunfire, the sound of bombings and large shells, all of these noises form a kind of melody that rocks us to sleep. Now that we don't hear the sound of gunfire, now that we can't hear the bombs anymore, we can't fall asleep. We are trying to sleep with silence, and it is taking us some time to get used to it.

While most Lebanese are trying to put the war behind them, young fighters will be haunted by images of violence and abuses of power for a long, long time. Many have come to regret their involvement in the war. All that the war has done to young fighters is destroy their ability to live in a normal environment. As Elie puts it,

I can't live normally anymore. I can't hold a job. I sleep all day. I am unable to take orders. It is all due to the war. It destroyed me. I wish I could go back and change what I have done.

Elie hopes that the experiences of his generation will serve as an example to others:

War is nothing, it destroys everything, it destroys society, it destroys souls. The further we keep away from it the better. I advise all young men of the age I was then [fourteen] to think very hard before they decide to carry a gun. Because they will achieve nothing by it. Everything goes on, society and industries go on, but it affects them personally. They can be sure that whatever they do in war will affect them in peace. Their future will be ruined.

If Elie only knew then what he knows now. (From Elie's scrapbook.)

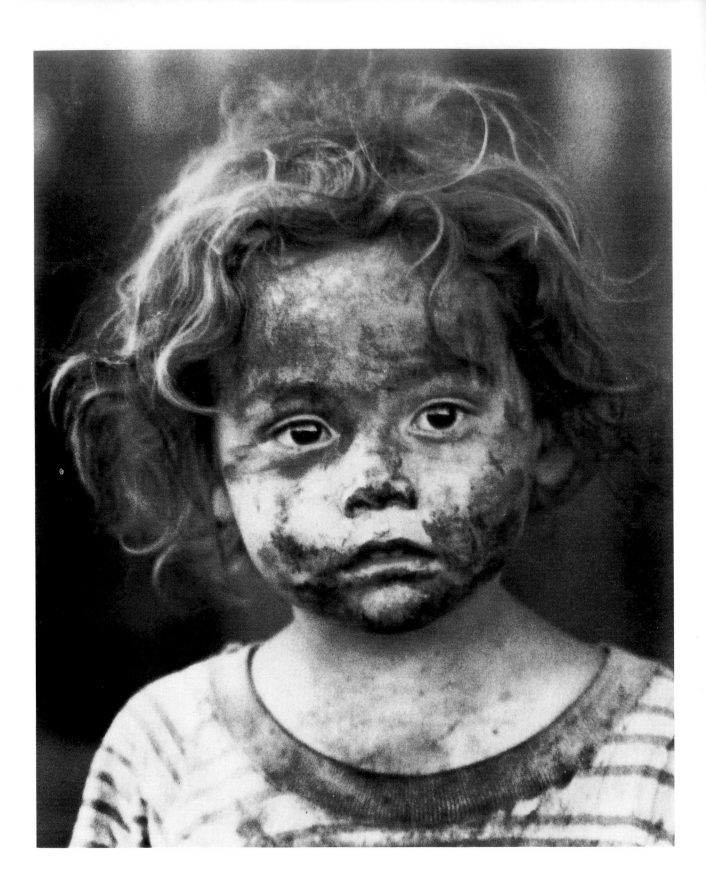

2

ambushed from abroad
el salvador

The helicopters suddenly appeared over the village of El Mozote, a remote village in El Salvador near the Honduran border. Inside the planes were the elite troops of an American-trained Salvadoran army unit returning from a firefight with a rebel group several miles away. Seemingly, they were coming to the village to spend the night and depart the next day.

Civil war had been raging in El Salvador since the 1970s, when poor people and students began demanding better working conditions and social equality. In the capital, San Salvador, university students, trade-union members, and laborers had demonstrated for social reform. These demonstrations were brutally repressed by the government. People were kidnaped, tortured, and killed by the government forces. Many of the victims were teenagers. With no other way to effect social change, thousands of people joined the rebels in the mountains. In response, the army took over the government in 1979 and began to intimidate or even murder any citizen they suspected of antigovernment activities.

While El Mozote was in the middle of a guerrilla area, the townspeople had, for the most part, tried to remain neutral. Several of the town's political leaders were friendly with influential government military officers. The government was aware that the villagers had tried to avoid taking sides. When fighting began in the nearby mountains, in December 1981, the village leaders persuaded the people to remain in their homes rather than flee. They assured them that nothing would happen.

When the army arrived in El Mozote, the soldiers were in an angry mood. Half the villagers—including women and children—were ordered to leave their homes and come into the town square. Rufina Amaya Márquez, the mother of three children, recalled how it began:

The army came in the afternoon. They told everyone to lie down on their faces. Even the children had to lie down in the street. They made them lie there for hours.

In many parts of El Salvador entire families were interrogated and arrested on suspicion of aiding the guerrillas.

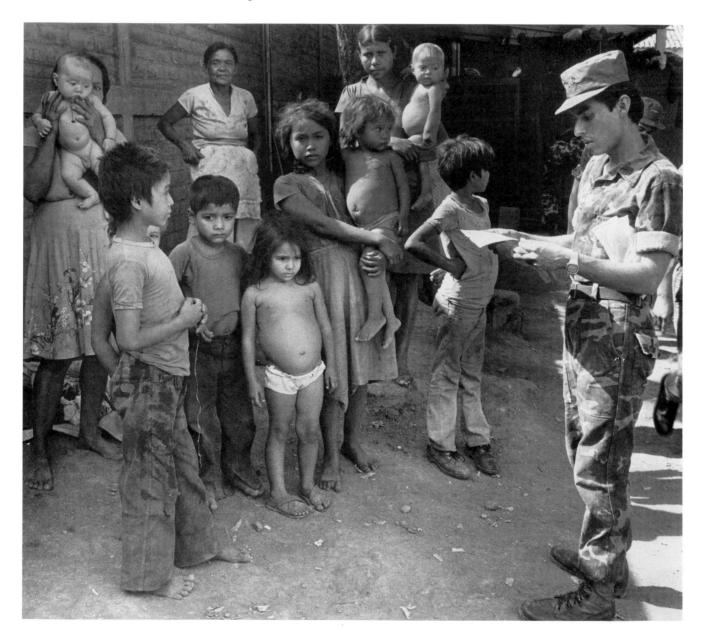

The soldiers roughly questioned adults, trying to get information about the rebels. But the people knew nothing. The soldiers threatened them. "We thought they were going to kill us all—that we were sentenced to die right there," Rufina said. But nothing happened that night. After hours of questioning, the villagers were sent back to their homes and told to stay there—or they would be shot. The people hoped that if they could get through the night safely, everything would be all right the next day.

It was early morning when the soldiers began pounding on the doors and ordering everyone out. For several hours, the villagers were forced to stand in the dark. The children were hungry and crying. When morning came, a helicopter arrived and a group of army officers descended and talked with the soldiers. The helicopters departed. And then the killings began.

The men were blindfolded and taken to the church. The women and children were crowded into a house. Rufina watched in horror as the soldiers began to kill the men, including her own husband. She later explained: "There was a window in the church and some of the women could see what was happening. They began screaming, 'Don't kill them. Don't kill them.'" Younger women were taken outside, raped, and then shot. Children were separated from their mothers. The women were questioned about the rebels and then taken to a house and shot. The soldiers burned houses in which people were hiding, and refused to allow them to escape.

The slaughter continued through the rest of the day. When most of the adults were dead, the soldiers turned to the children. Rufina, who had managed to hide, overheard a conversation between the soldiers about the children:

> "What shall we do with the children that are left," one asked? "We shall kill them because they can grow up and become guerrillas," another answered. "We'll take care of the job now." One soldier protested that he didn't want to kill kids. "Maybe we can take some," he said. "The order from the Colonel is to kill them all," the other answered. "And we have to complete our orders. And that's it."

Eight-year-old José Guevara was taken by the soldiers with a group of children. He carried his baby brother with him. As he watched the soldiers kill the children one by one, he made a decision to try and save his life.

A memorial for the innocent.

I watched them hang my brother. He was two years old. I could see that I was going to be killed soon, and I thought it would be better to die running. So I ran. I slipped through the soldiers and dived into the bushes. They fired into the bushes but none of their bullets hit me.

One hundred and twenty children were still alive after José escaped. The soldiers took them into the parish house and then massacred them all. One hundred and twenty children—dead. By nightfall, when the soldiers had finished their bloody work, over 800 people were dead. Only one child was left in the village, and he was crying. Rufina saw the soldiers shoot him. She managed to hide behind a tree during the slaughter, and then escaped. For four days she hid in the hills before she was helped.

The massacre at El Mozote, the worst of many such atrocities committed by the army of El Salvador, was part of a deliberate campaign to terrorize the people. As in all wars, people were killed by bombs, forced to leave their homes, and separated from their families. But in El Salvador there were also victims of another kind of war, the so-called "dirty war," in which people just disappeared—being taken away, tortured, and killed for no apparent reason.

Because the Salvadoran government characterized itself as anti-Communist, the United States gave more than $4 billion in economic and military aid to El Salvador to support the military regime. The aid made El Salvador a highly militarized society, and the Salvadoran armed forces grew from 8,000 to 56,000 troops. In the 1980s, many massacres took place; 75,000 people died, most of whom were civilians killed by the army and right-wing civilian "death squads" without any trial or proof of guilt. A rumor could become a death sentence.

Despite the killing, America's support continued. Throughout the 1980s, President Ronald Reagan requested, and the U.S. Congress approved, increasing levels of economic aid to El Salvador. When massacres were reported by journalists and other investigators, the U.S. government denied what had happened or tried to blame it on the rebels. Since the United States was supporting the Salvadoran military with money and training, such atrocities were an embarrassment. Rather than find out the facts, U.S. officials chose to deny the truth of the reports.

Meanwhile, young men and women in El Salvador were dragged out of their homes in the middle of the night and taken away, never to be seen alive again. One mother spoke of her son.

Since the government denied that the massacre occurred, archaeological methods were used to uncover the truth *(facing page)*.

They came in the middle of the night. They had their faces covered, and machine guns. They came into the house and dragged him out of his bed. It happened on June 12, 1976, and I am still waiting. Sometimes I get word that they might have found his body and I go to see and it is some other kid, not mine.

Parents, friends, and children of people who disappeared feel guilty, believing they should somehow have prevented the killing. They also feel guilty for having survived. Delores, a sixty-five-year-old woman from San Salvador, is a member of COMADRE (Committee of Mothers and Relatives of Political Prisoners and Political Murder Victims of El Salvador). This group has tried—and is still trying—to fight the arbitrary arrests and disappearance of innocent civilians like Delores's son.

War weary.

One day they took my son with three of his friends. It was Easter in 1978. For a whole year I did not hear anything about it; I went to the authorities with my questions, but nobody would answer us. A year later one woman from COMADRE came and said they found three bodies in this place called La Cruz. I went to see and one of the three bodies was my son. My son was killed because he believed in social justice and equality. I wish they had taken me instead of him.

Keeping the memory alive: A mother who lost her child when he was arbitrarily arrested and murdered by the death squads.

Paulo is a seventeen-year-old boy who lives in the town of Suchitoto; he feels that the poor are always vulnerable:

You don't know what it is like to live without any protection. We are poor and no one listens to us. If we are killed or tortured no one cares. So many of our friends and relatives were killed by the death squads. I don't particularly like the guerrillas, but when you see what the government has done you have to support them.

Ignacio is sixteen and lives in Haciendita, a guerrilla community. He remembers things he wishes he had never seen.

The army came into the villages and killed many people. They would torture people in terrible ways. You knew there was nothing you could do about it.

Pablo is also sixteen and lives in the same community as Ignacio. He hid in a cornfield for a whole day during an attack, and came back to find his father dead.

Because we lived in guerrilla areas, the army assumed that we are with them. I am not saying that we are against them, but my father never fought with the guerrillas. He just helped them with food and things, and they killed him anyway because they never bothered to ask.

What is now a workplace for children used to be a hiding place during attacks *(facing page).*

A boy scout carries a wounded woman on his back after sniper fire broke up a funeral mass for slain archbishop Oscar Romero at the Metropolitan Cathedral.

Young people were often the targets of government forces.

The government did not hesitate to kill anyone who disagreed with it. Soldiers even murdered and raped nuns and killed priests. Before his government-backed assassination on March 24, 1980, Archbishop Oscar Romero of El Salvador, a hero to many poor people, made a speech sharply criticizing the United States for supporting the killing. Romero was killed, like many others, for having given his opinion and for opposing the actions of his government.

Government brutality drove many young people, even if they were not Communists, to join the guerrillas. Rebecca was a college student when she realized she could no longer bear the tyranny. Joining the guerrillas made her feel liberated:

When I first joined the guerrillas it was like my first love. I had the feeling that I was beginning something new, something totally different. It gave my life meaning. It was the greatest experience I have ever known.

Students were a main target of brutality. Clelia, who was fourteen when she joined, did so because she saw the police beating her fellow students during a demonstration. She was nearly killed in combat.

The enemy spotted us. There were a small number of us and two were hurt badly. I was wounded and it was difficult for my companions to get me out of the combat zone. I was wounded in the neck, and the bullet grazed my lungs.

Two days later Clelia was rescued.

Anyone who had a friend or relative suspected of being sympathetic to the guerrillas was in danger. One young woman, who preferred not to be identified, said that she was warned the death squads were after her because of the actions of one of her relatives. One day she was in San Salvador when a death squad came for her.

Young orphans.

I boarded the bus and two men followed me. One passed by me and let me feel his gun against my back. He said, "This is for you." So I got off the bus. They did too. Then I hopped back on the bus and lost them. The bus driver realized what was happening so he drove past the next two stops and pulled alongside a taxi and told me to get out quick. I could see solidarity in his face, and he understood what was happening.

Sometimes young children showed tremendous courage in the face of death. Eight-year-old Maria was running away from the soldiers with her mother.

I was running along just at my mother's side when she was hit by a bullet in the back. I said, "Momma, they shot you." Perhaps she hadn't felt it yet because she kept running. Now she couldn't run anymore. She gave me the knapsack and told me to go on.

Maria managed to escape and hide. While she was in hiding, she saw a soldier shoot a six-year-old boy, leaving him for dead. But when Maria went to him, she saw he was still alive. She bandaged him, cleaned his wound, and then carried him for two days until she found help. Later she found her mother's body. Maria's mother had survived being shot, but not the cruel treatment she suffered afterwards.

In 1992, with the end of the Cold War with the Soviet Union, and with Congress concerned about the continual government massacres, the Salvadoran civil war finally ended. But while the outright killing stopped, the suffering continued. Almost half of El Salvador's people are still unemployed. Even children must work for practically nothing in order to eat. In cities like San Salvador, they beg on the streets, watch over parked cars, and sell lottery tickets. Some are even willing to sacrifice their health and lives to earn a few dollars: They entertain people by putting gasoline in their mouths and then blowing it on a flame, like circus performers. Gas blowers do not live very long. They get sick and die from lung infections.

Rafael is eight years old and has been blowing gas for several years. He has no other way to earn money. Every day he buys a little gas and waits at the side of the road, sometimes all night, for people to pay him money to entertain them by blowing gas. After every performance he spits on the ground to get rid of the burning and pain. Rafael considers himself lucky to earn a living—even though it will eventually kill him.

Performing on the streets *(above)*. Rafael sometimes stays up all night, earning only a few dollars.

Like all children around the world, children in refugee communities still have the energy to play.

Children of coal mer-
chants play near their
parents' shop *(facing
page)*.

I have no choice but to blow gas. My father is dead and my mother really needs the money to survive. My brother does the same thing as I do. We are refugees here, and I am forced to work. It burns my mouth and I know it might kill me, but I really do not have a choice.

Street children can earn a maximum of three dollars a day. Beggars usually make more money than those who work.

Most street children come from the countryside and have lost their families. Some do not know where or when they were born. But not all displaced children end up on the streets. Many stay with their families and live in refugee camps. They lead a difficult and uncertain life. During the war, more than 500,000 Salvadorans left their homes; most were fleeing guerrilla-controlled areas that were constantly shelled by government forces. Many refugees walked for miles at night and hid during the day to avoid being killed. Sometimes people walked for weeks with little food or water. Mothers had to keep their babies from crying, or the whole family would be discovered. Family members not strong enough to make the journey were left behind.

Today, while some villagers have returned to their homes and are rebuilding their lives, others still live in poor, rat-infested shantytowns all around the cities. Their living conditions are terrible and their prospects for the future almost nonexistent. Children in refugee communities live in tin houses, without beds, running water, or heat. The camps are dirty and badly kept. Most refugees were farmers who wanted to work their land and raise their families. Now they and their children live like outcasts in the slums. Mara is twelve and lives in a refugee community in San Salvador.

When you live like us in refugee communities, you are not a real part of the society. Our life is different than the life of other people. We are not from San Salvador and do not go to school, so we have no friends outside the camp. We go out for a walk but our life is really in the camp. We have been here for 7 years.

About 1 million Salvadorans left their country and immigrated to the United States or nearby countries like Guatemala, Honduras, Belize, and Panama. Since the United States rarely allowed the refugees to enter legally, even though many were in danger of being killed, most came as illegal aliens. Families were separated. Sometimes mothers were caught

and returned, while their children escaped and remained. Many feared that government forces would arrest and torture family members and friends back home to take revenge on those who fled. Julio is now eighteen, but when he came to America he was just a little boy who was fleeing his homeland and fearing the worst. He felt guilty and scared about leaving his grandfather:

When we left for America my grandfather stayed behind because he did not want to leave. The whole time we were in the United States we never spoke to him. It was terrible for us to imagine what could be happening to him. I used to imagine the worst.

Some refugees have made new lives for themselves in America. Others have returned to El Salvador or plan to do so. But many who return, like Pablo, feel they have no future in either country.

I would like to make something out of my life and get an education. During the war we did not get a chance to go to school. I hardly know how to read and write. I would take care of my mother like she took care of me. I really love her very much. If I had a wife I would give her everything and I would make sure that she doesn't go through what my mother had to go through.

Without a future, children like Bernardo are still haunted by the past.

Now that the war is over I always dream of violence. I always wake up in the middle of the night because I imagine that there is someone who is trying to get inside to kill my whole family. I wake up sweating, and I am happy when I find out that it was just a dream.

Bernardo also has a hard time concentrating in school.

Teachers came to give us lessons, to teach us about things. But I couldn't focus and concentrate on what they said.

On March 20, 1994, the people of El Salvador voted in presidential elections under the supervision of the United Nations. During the war, anyone who wanted to vote was caught in a bind. Since the only candidates one could vote for were those supported by the government, *not* voting was interpreted by the army as a sign of sympathy for the rebels.

From battleground to playground (*facing page*).

Salvadoran Army soldiers used mind games to win children over to their side.

A child returns to her village to find nothing left *(facing page)*.

However, voting was interpreted by the guerrillas as a sign of sympathy for the dictatorship. Either way, you could get killed.

In recent elections, political slogans in the capital of San Salvador told people to begin thinking about the future and putting the past behind them. However, it is difficult for many to have faith in the government. "Before, we were bothered all the time [by war]," said a woman in the city of San Miguel, who did not want to give her name. "Now we are happier, but the elections, who knows? Only God knows if it will make our lives better."

Today, El Salvador seems like a peaceful small country in Central America, with beautiful sandy beaches and green mountains. It has colorful villages with mud houses painted in many different colors. Yet some villages remain deserted. There are no children playing, only an occasional dog seen on a country road. Many young victims are still found in mass graves. Most were not part of the rebel movement, yet they were tortured and violated in the most inhuman way. Their memories and sto-

Young field workers wait for a bus at the end of a long day.

ries are kept alive by their mothers, who with great courage started COMADRE. The members of this group are trying to find out what happened to their children so they can give them a decent burial. For many years, it was very risky to ask any such questions. And even today, young people are cautious when describing what happened to them.

But, at the same time, they want their tragic experience to have meaning for others. José says he would like to send a message to the children of America.

I would like to tell children who live in peace how it was, what it was like to be in a state of war where people are killed left and right. When people are tortured, burned, hurt. I would like them to feel what I felt to see that they should fight with other children to stop the wars.

Many Americans and Salvadorans feel that when a powerful nation like the United States makes a decision to involve itself in a conflict, it should think of the consequences to the people and especially the children involved in the conflict. U.S. Senator Brock Adams has stated:

It is true that our [U.S.] security is linked to the security of the people of El Salvador, but what too many people fail to realize is that ultimately our security is threatened, not strengthened, when our foreign policy is immoral. Our security cannot be founded on massacres, torture and imprisonment in another nation. When we claim to be supporting democracy overseas, while in truth we are aiding an army which regards unarmed children as military targets, our moral basis for leadership is eroded.

Some children of El Salvador are bitter toward America for financing the war and denying the truth of what happened to the people. Others, like Pablo, are kinder:

I don't think Americans know where their money was going all those years, because they would have never supported the government if they knew of the killings and the massacres.

Survival is tough for children fending for themselves on the streets of San Salvador, but life is slowly returning to normal.

3

children killing children

mozambique

Imagine that one day, while you arc playing in the street, a group of soldiers suddenly appear, line up your parents, brothers, and sisters against a wall, and, putting a gun in your hand, tell you: "Kill them if you want to live." What would you do? This was a decision that thousands of children were forced to face in the Mozambican war.

Many foreign journalists experienced in covering conflicts throughout the world have said that the war in Mozambique was the worst they had ever seen. Children were deliberately brutalized—broken down and then rebuilt into ruthless soldiers. They were denied access to medical care and left to die from disease and starvation. In some regions people were forced to wear plastic bags because they did not have any clothes. Civilians were treated in the most atrocious fashion: kidnaped, tortured, massacred. Between 1981 and 1986, more than 1,000,000 people were killed, 320,000 of them children. War and famine have given this country one of the highest infant-mortality rates in Africa as well as one of the lowest life expectancies. Most Americans live to be over seventy, while most Mozambicans don't survive to their fortieth birthday. They die very young because of poverty, disease, and the deadly after-effects of war. Faced with such horror for so many years, Mozambican children have buried their emotions deep inside. They speak in a matter-of-fact way, keeping their feelings hidden because the reality of their lives is too terrible to face.

Hungry children collect grains of rice that fell off a truck delivering food.

The civil war began shortly after the country gained its independence. For about 450 years, Mozambique, located on the southern coast of East Africa, was a colony of Portugal. There was always some opposition to the Portuguese presence in Mozambique, but in the 1960s, resistance became intense. Several revolutionary groups joined together to form the Mozambique Liberation Front, or FRELIMO. In 1975, the Portuguese finally withdrew, and FRELIMO gained control of the country.

Mozambique faced many problems. The Portuguese did not leave behind any educational or medical institutions, as the French and the British did in the countries they colonized. No political structure had been set in place. To prevent total chaos, FRELIMO began to rule with an iron fist. They set up a Marxist government with strong ties to what was then the Soviet Union. The government began to experiment with social changes that proved economically disastrous. Opposition parties were banned and, according to the human-rights organization Amnesty International, thousands were killed and tens of thousands arrested.

Repression often leads to resistance. In 1977, a resistance movement was formed and began to attack government forces. It was called the Mozambique National Resistance Organization (RENAMO). However, RENAMO was more than just an opposition group. It was financed and organized by Mozambique's neighbor Rhodesia, which was then under white control. The Rhodesian government was worried because a militant African state with ties to the Soviet Union was on its border. It hoped to weaken or overthrow the FRELIMO government by backing RENAMO.

When Rhodesia (now called Zimbabwe) changed its government to have majority rule, RENAMO turned to South Africa, another neighbor, which was then controlled by whites. During the 1980s South Africa built up RENAMO and the civil war escalated. The killings and the destruction of the country intensified.

The war was mainly fought in the countryside and shattered the lives of the rural population. The rebels, also called Bandidos Armados (Armed Bandits), imposed a policy of terror on rural areas and ended up controlling most of the countryside. RENAMO would attack train convoys and massacre all the passengers. Over a period of ten years brutal attacks on villages occurred daily, usually at dawn. The fighters were merciless. Soldiers came into villages and burned, ransacked, or killed everything and everyone they could get their hands on. As a result of the attacks, more than 3.4 million people sought refuge in six nearby countries (Swaziland, Zimbabwe, South Africa, Tanzania, Zambia, and Malawi). Many of

Former RENAMO soldiers waiting in a demobilization camp before they return to civilian life.

them fled through jungle areas and risked being killed by wild animals rather than be trapped in the fighting. Another 3 million were displaced inside Mozambique. More than 40 percent of displaced people were children. By targeting civilians, RENAMO victimized the most vulnerable segment of the population.

RENAMO was merciless toward children, torturing and slaughtering them. Sometimes RENAMO soldiers would force children to set fire to their homes with their parents inside; sometimes they would force them to kill their parents with machetes; and sometimes they would kill the parents themselves and then chop them to pieces in front of the children. After such attacks the terrorized children were kidnaped by RENAMO, to serve either on military bases or in combat. Those children, after being trained, would become ruthless killing machines—the much feared "wolf children" of Mozambique.

Ricardo is fifteen years old today and lives in an orphanage in the suburbs of Mozambique's capital, Maputo. He was kidnaped by RENAMO soldiers when he was five years old.

> *They came into our villages and massacred everyone. My parents were able to run away; I ran with them but I lost them. Then they captured all the boys they hadn't killed, and took us with them. We walked for many days with no food or drink. We drank urine when there was some. If any of us showed signs of weakness they would kill us. Running away was out of the question.*

The kidnaped children were usually taken to a region where they did not know the language. (There are more than sixty different dialects in Mozambique.) Tearing them away from their families and communities made them much easier to control. The children underwent inhuman military training and, in their isolation and suffering, began to look up to their superior officers. They were brainwashed by their captors, who wanted to control their minds. Laura Nhangale, a captive for 19 months, explained:

> *They kept talking to us about a new life and telling us that they were fighting to liberate the country from FRELIMO. There were a lot of meetings to explain the new life. They said it will take you out of your suffering. They wanted you to be happy. If you seemed unhappy, then they say you are planning to run away. . . . If you are sad, it means you don't like the new life.*

Trained to become killers, many RENAMO children, even those as young as eight, committed some of the most horrible acts in the Mozambican war. They were tremendously feared by civilians. They seemed to have lost the ability to distinguish between right and wrong and were able to commit the most gruesome acts without flinching. Killing and torturing people became common for many of these children. Having witnessed or been forced to commit acts of extreme violence on their own parents at a very young age, these children grew up with no emotional bonds. Like Ricardo, they often justified their acts on the grounds that they were only obeying orders.

I was a soldier. I lost my finger in combat. I killed many people. I was told to do it, so I did it. Those were the rules. I was ordered and I obeyed.

Not every child blamed his actions on others. Anastasio, who was made into a soldier at seven, feels remorse for what he did.

I feel responsible for what I have done. I killed two people. It was my fault not my superior officers' fault. I am responsible for my actions.

Ricardo (right), a former wolf child, trying to get used to his new life in an orphanage in the suburbs of Maputo.

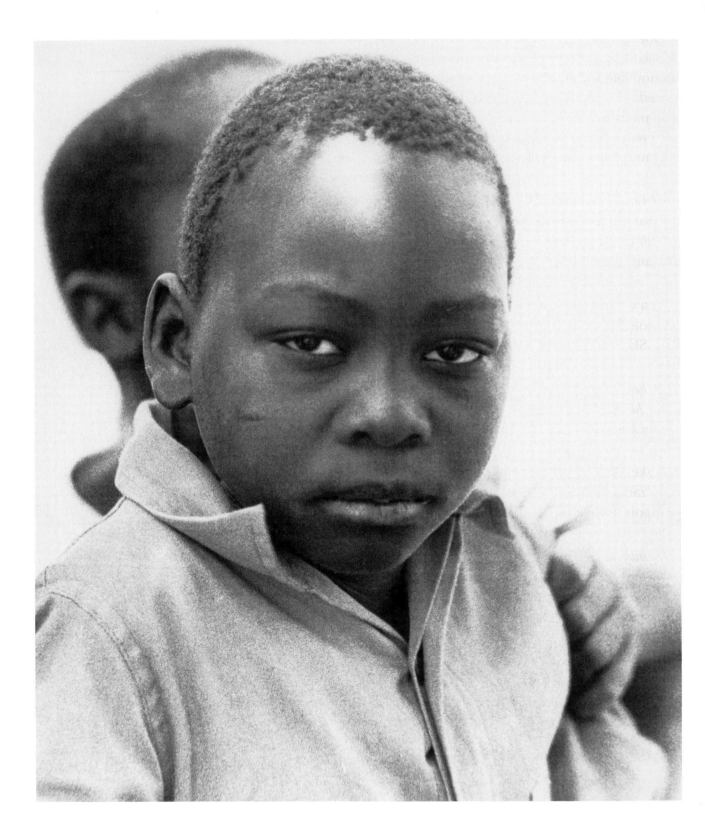

Not all children abducted by RENAMO became soldiers. Many were used as slaves, and were abused and mistreated. Life on the military bases was horrible for children. They were barely fed and were constantly terrorized. Liza was kidnaped with her sister and two of her brothers after their parents were killed in front of them. She lived with RENAMO for three years. She and her brother Joaquim were the only two who survived. They now live in an orphanage in the province of Tete.

At Casa Banana [the headquarters of RENAMO], we were used as slaves. I was just ten years old and I was raped repeatedly. The officers would sleep with all the girls. It was very difficult. They used to hurt us. They would change wives all the time.

Ana was twelve when a RENAMO soldier her own age raped her and then told her that they were married. A year later, she gave birth to his child. She wanted to run away but felt trapped:

He held my throat the first time. After that we were married. He was a soldier but he was there a lot of the time in the village. I couldn't leave. I didn't even know where I was so where could I go?

Abubaker Sultan, who works for the Save the Children Foundation, an organization trying to help children like Ana, says that the only way that many young girls could survive was through sex.

In order to have access to food, in order not to get killed, girls had to have the protection of someone powerful, a soldier. Sex brought protection so the girls allowed themselves to be sexually abused. It's a serious problem. You have many young girls with babies. In most cases the father is not identified.

Captives were organized into work brigades. They were ordered to clean, cook, and take care of soldiers. The work brigades ate and slept together. Since food was a rare commodity, they were often sent to bring some back by any means. If they returned empty-handed they were beaten.

Although life in the camps was very hard, most remained because those camps were the only home they had. But a few were willing to risk everything for a chance for freedom. Liza was one:

Scarred for life: Anastasio *(facing page).*

I ended up running away from the RENAMO base. One time they had sent us to get some water, without any supervision. So I never went back. I walked for two months in the jungle. I didn't have anything to eat. I almost died of starvation. This period is still my most horrible memory.

The risk of escape was great. Anyone caught was executed in front of the others. Laura recalls:

The first thing they tell you is that if you try and escape, we'll kill you. Any arguments, they kill you. Any problems, you are killed.

Even though RENAMO was responsible for most of the atrocities in the Mozambican civil war, the government forces also did their share of harm. Dodo and his father were arrested and imprisoned by FRELIMO forces after his father was accused of being a RENAMO informer. He was only seven years old.

We were put in jail for a few weeks. Then someone came and told us we were going to be judged in another town. So they opened the cell and let us out. We were ten [meaning: There were ten of us]. We were crammed into a car and driven away. Suddenly the soldier who was driving turned left and drove towards the river. Everyone started screaming. The two militaries stopped the car, got out, and began calling people one by one. They shot each one in the head and threw their bodies in the river. They also shot my father. I was the last one. The officer decided to keep me to take care of his house.

In 1992, a drought devastated the country, causing great suffering on both sides. Farmers fled the land, and starvation threatened everyone. RENAMO finally agreed to end its resistance. At last the massacres were over, and Mozambique began to emerge from its time of horror. The peace agreement was signed in Rome in October 1992 by the head of RENAMO, Alfonso Dhlakama, and the president of Mozambique, Joaquim Chissano.

The war's end, however has not ended the suffering. For one thing, there is the refugee problem. During the war millions of people fled to neighboring countries, often walking for days without food or drink before reaching their destination. Many died on the way or were captured by RENAMO. And the ones who reached the many refugee camps have been living there for a long time. Now they are returning to a country

Conditions in the refugee camps make children vulnerable to disease *(facing page)*.

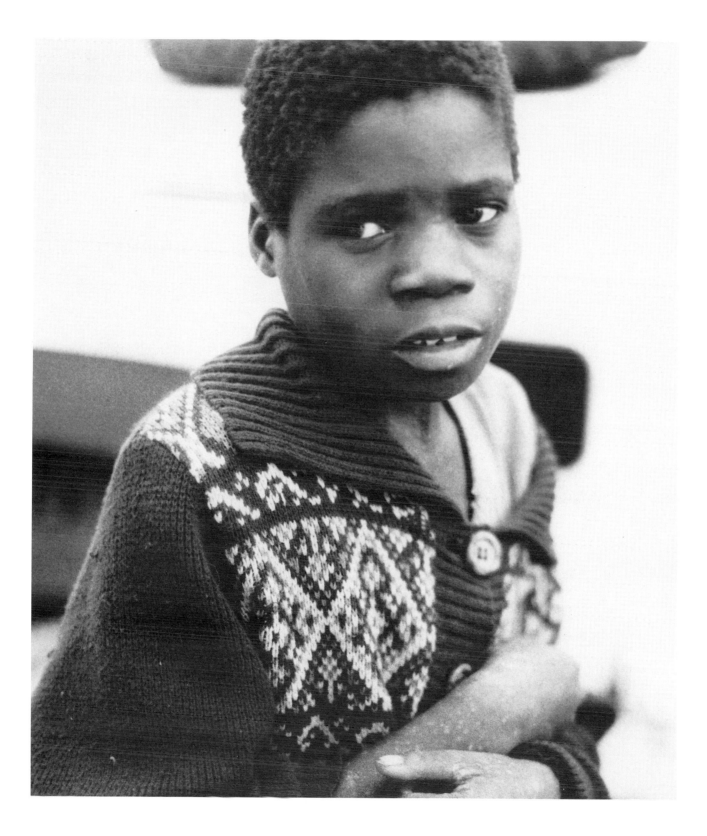

with no infrastructure. Some are even carrying back the roofs of their houses with them, because they know that they won't be able to build new ones at home. Some children, like eight-year-old Carlos, have never been to Mozambique. They were born in refugee camps and spent their childhood there. Says Carlos,

My parents were exiled in the war. They had to run away. Me and my brothers were born in the refugee camp in Malawi. I just know the name of my village, nothing else. People say my country is destroyed.

Carlos says it is hard for children to grow up in a refugee camp. You never know how long you will be allowed to stay, and you're always waiting for the convoys to bring food:

You hardly ever go to school. All you do is sit around the camp and wait. Wait for food, wait for water, wait for something better.

Now that the war is over, many refugees have returned, walking for many long days through the jungle to reach their homes, where their ancestors are buried. But many refugees are forced to wait in transit camps once they reach Mozambique. Sometimes, like Toca, they wait because there are too many land mines.

I am from Villanova. We can't go back to our village because of mines. Already many of our family returned to our village and are dead.

In the northern part of Toca's village red signs with a drawing of a skull warn the civilian population of the presence of land mines. The signs say "DANGER CHIMBAMBAIRA!" There is no word for "mines" in the local language, Bantu, so they are called *chimbambaira,* or "big sweet potato." No one would suspect that such a beautiful landscape contains devices that will mutilate and kill the local population for many years to come. When children in Mozambique walk outside their villages, they tread lightly. One false step, a little too much pressure on the earth—and then suddenly *boom!* There is an explosion, and a limb—or a life—is lost.

In Mozambique today there are an estimated 2 million land mines, ready to blow up on contact. In most wars, mines are used as a defensive weapon to kill enemy soldiers, and their positions are marked on maps so they can be removed at the end of the conflict. In Mozambique, no markings were made, and mines were buried haphazardly to kill civilians. Hav-

Children are so poor that
they cannot afford to buy
clothes *(left)*.

Human skeleton found in
a mine field.

ing no self-destructive mechanisms, they remain active until they are removed by de-mining specialists or exploded by a victim. Walking in the bush, or even on roads, has become a nightmare. Forty-four percent of Mozambique's people are children. In the countryside the number of children who have lost an arm or a leg is truly alarming. And the number of mine victims has tripled since the end of the war. Some 200,000 people and children have already lost their lives or been seriously injured by the leftover mines. A former United Nations High Commissioner for Refugees has commented:

> *It is a real tragedy. It is as if this land is cursed. Because the locations of the mines have not been marked on any maps, it will take many years and millions of dollars to demine the totality of this country. In the meantime, children will still get killed, mutilated, and injured. Mozambique is not ready to face such a situation. Medical facilities are destroyed and the ones that are not are ill equipped. Many victims end up dying as a result of secondary infections.*

Another problem that persists despite the war's end is that many children live in poverty, with little food to eat and few clothes to wear. Dodo lives in an orphanage; he does not have to worry about food, so he is able to talk about his feelings. Many other children are too worried about eating to talk about what they feel inside. The moral and psychological damage they have suffered is often worse than their physical problems. Many children have constant headaches, bad dreams, heart pains, and persistent flashbacks to the murder of their brothers, sisters, mothers, and fathers. Psychologists say that it is very difficult to assess the long-term effects of such experiences. Children who have suffered under such extreme conditions are often marked for life. It is undeniable that Mozambican children will relive their experiences for many years to come and have had their view of the world altered forever. Some, like Dodo, will hate for the rest of their lives. Every night, Dodo dreams of his father's body being thrown into the river. He will never forget that image and will never forgive the murderers. He is very grateful to the people who have rescued him and taken care of him. He longs for a family life and every night cries himself to sleep.

Forgive! Are you kidding! Never! I want revenge. I want justice. I have no father anymore and I don't think it's fair.

Collecting wood in a mine field can be deadly (*facing page*).

Joaquim, who now lives in an orphanage with his sister Liza, also cannot
forgive.

> *I will never forget what the RENAMO did to my parents. I will never forgive
> them. After we were kidnaped, I took one brother and Liza and another
> sister. They all died of starvation except Liza.*

Along with feelings of revenge or pain, former child-soldiers also have
deep feelings of regret. Pablo is nine and spent most of his childhood
fighting for RENAMO. Today he wishes he could have another chance to
regain the innocence that was stolen from him. "When I grow up I just
want to be a little kid."

Many of RENAMO's young victims ended up in refugee camps in foreign countries. But most often children ended up living on the streets of
the cities. When rebel forces attacked villages people ran in all directions,
and often lost track of one another. Most street children don't know if
their parents are alive or dead, and they don't know how to find them.
The International Committee of the Red Cross has organized a program
of family reunification, but according to them it will be almost impossible
to reunite all children with their families.

In the meantime, children forced to live on the streets and fend for
themselves have no choice but to take what the cities can offer them. On

Reenacting war memories
(facing page).

Street children have made
their home in a garbage
dump.

Sleeping to forget.

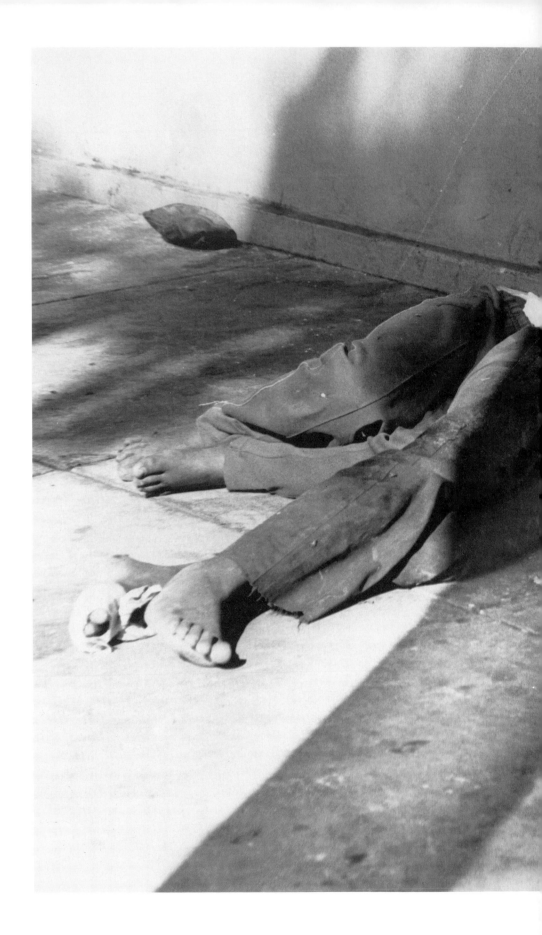

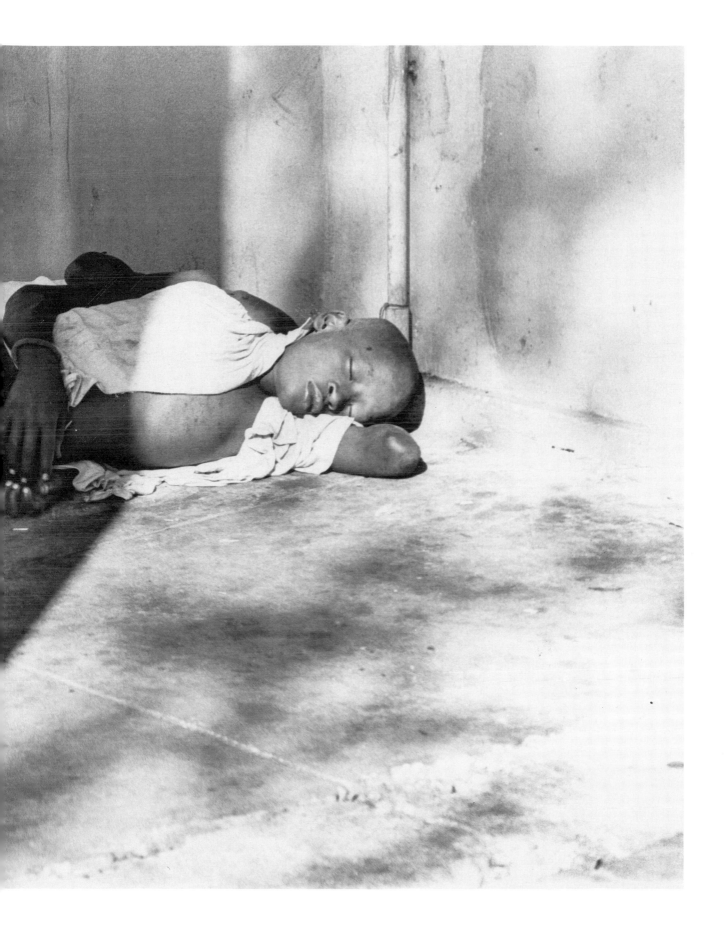

Making toys out of nothing *(above)*.

Flies settle on the mouth of a child sleeping on the street.

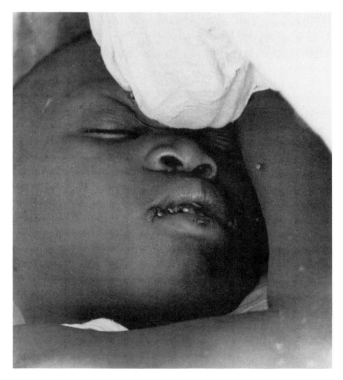

the streets of Maputo, they sleep on sidewalks, beg, and eat poorly. Many have a variety of skin, lung, and sexually transmitted diseases. To survive, they run errands, prostitute themselves, beg, watch cars, carry bags, and search for their families. To amuse themselves they make toys out of wire and empty cans they find in trash and try to sell them to visitors. During the war, they used to make toy guns, tanks, and hand grenades. Today they make toy ambulances and U.N. relief helicopters. Never having had toys to play with, Mozambican children are very creative, and the toys they built out of almost nothing are works of art.

Amoro is ten, and has been living on the streets of Maputo for five years.

I came here to escape war and famine. It took me days to arrive. I walked, ran, hitchhiked. I finally caught a bus that brought me to the capital. I don't know what happened to my family. I was only five when our village was attacked. I don't know if my parents would recognize me if they saw me.

Like most Mozambican children, those who live on the street do not go to school. Most of them don't know how to read and write, since schools were destroyed during the war, and many teachers were killed. They have no roof over their heads but they feel that their situation is better in the city than it was in their villages, where the war left nothing but misery. Most of their villages have been destroyed, their houses burned, and the crops killed by drought. Many street children feel lucky that they can sometimes find food to eat in the garbage cans of the cities. But even though they are safer on the streets than at home, they have no parents to care for and protect them. Feliz describes how his chances to survive are better in the streets of the cities than at home.

Here in the capital, you can always find food. You stand outside restaurants, outside the market, you always find something to eat. In our villages, there is nothing. People are being killed. The drought and the war made it impossible for people to move around in search of food, so everyone is starving.

Feliz sells cigarettes one by one. He sometimes smokes one to feel grown up. But Feliz and his friends are still children. Children who get scared at night, children who need their parents, a home, and security.

Adult gestures.

Children waiting for a
food convoy (*facing page*).

When I close my eyes to go to sleep, I try to think of my mother. So I can feel protected.

The voices of Mozambican children are not the same as those of other children. They have suffered so much that their voices are muffled. They describe what they have been through without showing their feelings, partly out of pride and partly because of the pain. But what they have to say is enough to convey the horrors of war. Mozambican children will need help to forget their experiences and live in peace. Clearly, it will take a very long time for Mozambique and its citizens to recover from the war. What happened in Mozambique should never be allowed to happen again. The children of Mozambique have a right to be happy. It will take a very long time for them to forget what they have been through. It will take a very long time for them to trust in the future.

4

the enemy next door
bosnia-herzegovina

On December 4, 1991, an eleven-year-old girl wrote in her diary, which she called Mimmy, thoughts that any American girl might express.

I'm writing to you from bed dear diary. . . . My favorite doll is snoozing on the little table. I'm now listening to Michael Jackson, "Man in the Mirror," I just had a crazy idea. I'm going to try and join Madonna's fan club. I really am crazy.

Six months later, she wrote:

I'm trying to concentrate so I can do my homework but I simply can't. Something is going on in town. You can hear gunfire from the hills. You feel that something is coming, something very bad. My stomach is in knots and I can't concentrate on my homework anymore.
   Mimmy, I'm afraid of WAR!!!

The writer of the diary is Zlata Filipovic, a Muslim girl who once lived in the city of Sarajevo, in the newly created country of Bosnia-Herzegovina. Like any other adolescent Zlata worried about her grades and thought about boys, parties, her favorite rock stars, skiing in the mountains, and swimming at the beach. But in the spring of 1992, her peaceful life came to an end: A vicious civil war broke out.

Zlata was born in a country that until recently was part of Yugoslavia. But even though Yugoslavia was one country, its people were composed of three main ethnic groups that had their own traditions and languages—the Serbians, the Croatians, and the Muslims. (There was also a smaller community of Macedonians.) They lived in six republics within Yugoslavia, some of which had two or more ethnic groups within their boundaries. While on the surface the different ethnic groups generally seemed to get along, and had even intermarried, there were deep divisions among them. As long as Yugoslavia had a strong ruler, these divisions were kept under control.

In 1984, three years after Zlata was born, the Winter Olympic games took place in Sarajevo, then the capital of Yugoslavia. The country was proud of the fact that it had been chosen as the site of the games. All groups worked together to make that year's Winter Olympics special. Everybody in Yugoslavia watched with pride as athletes of many different nationalities came to Sarajevo to demonstrate their excellence. And the visitors regarded Yugoslavia as a country where Serbs, Croats, and Muslims lived together harmoniously. But ten years later, those very people were in a bloody civil war that killed or wounded hundreds of thousands and created millions of refugees.

How did this happen in so short a time? The war was one of the tragic consequences of the collapse of communism in Eastern Europe and the Soviet Union. Yugoslavia had been a Communist country. When its political system fell apart in the late 1980s, the country began to divide along ethnic lines. Each republic held an election to determine its future. In 1991, Croatia and Slovenia, which had a majority of Croats, seceded from Yugoslavia. That same year, civil war broke out between the Croats and the Serbs living in Croatia. When Bosnia-Herzegovina seceded from Yugoslavia, it caused even greater turmoil. Large numbers of Muslims, Serbs, and Croats lived in Bosnia-Herzegovina. War broke out among the three ethnic groups to see who would control the newly independent state. No group wanted to live as a minority under the rule of a different nationality, for fear of being persecuted. Croat and Serb leaders stirred up ethnic hatred by playing on these fears.

Civilians became the first casualties of the war. People of one ethnic group were ruthlessly killed or forced to leave their homes by people of another group. The goal was to create ethnically "pure" communities—so that the Serb section would have only Serbs, the Croat section

Zlata Filipovic wrote about her life in war-torn Sarajevo as her friends were killed and injured (*facing page*).

A young child looks through a bullet hole in the window of her Sarajevo home weeks after her father was killed.

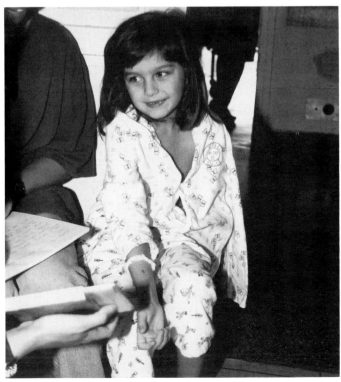

Children act out the war around them on the streets of Sarajevo *(top)*.

Isolating the various communities: A destroyed bridge in Capljina *(above left)*.

Manuela, seven years old, lost her arm in shelling aimed directly at children *(right)*.

only Croats, and the Muslim section only Muslims. This practice, called ethnic cleansing, was devastating, because Muslims, Croats, and Serbs had lived together for years in a number of villages.

This sudden hostility between groups violently disrupted the world of children. Zlata, who lived in Sarajevo, found herself a prisoner in her own apartment. For almost a year, Serbian gunners shelled the city from the surrounding hills. The shelling might come at any time. It could suddenly stop for several days and start again without warning. Snipers were everywhere. Day by day, the world around Zlata deteriorated. All the windows in her parents' beautiful apartment were blown out by the shelling. Only one room was considered safe to live in. Her parents could no longer go to work. Supplies ran low. Much of the time the family ate tasteless cheese and bread, which her parents risked their lives to buy. There was no water for bathing or flushing the toilet. There was seldom gas, electricity, or telephone service. Schools were closed, and children had to stay indoors for months at a time. Those who ventured outside might be killed by snipers or shells. Zlata recorded one such tragedy in her diary:

A girl, a medical student was KILLED. Her blood spilled out on the bridge.
In her final moments, all she said was, "Is this Sarajevo? HORRIBLE!
HORRIBLE! HORRIBLE!
NO ONE HERE AND NOTHING HERE IS NORMAL.

Several months later a friend of Zlata's was in the park where they used to play together. A shell exploded nearby, and a piece of shrapnel struck Zlata's friend in the head. It killed her.

When the shelling began, children and their families went to their cellars. They often stood in the dark, holding on to each other in silence, while the heavy guns thundered death and destruction around them. Houses were blown apart. Old people, young people, men, women, children, dogs, and cats—all blown apart. The shell doesn't care whom it kills.

For a long time, Yugoslavia's children will carry memories of hiding in a bomb shelter and being scared. They often have nightmares and wake up in the middle of the night screaming. In some cities, such as Sarajevo and Mostar, children experience constant shelling. They are used to running into the shelter, if anyone can get used to it. Although they dread the experience, gradually it becomes a way of life. Duje remembered living there as if he was in another world:

I was watching TV when the shelling started. They started shelling the village a little above my house. We had to go into the cellar of the hotel nearby. We spent fifteen days in the cellar. There were about 100 people. When we tried to go to the restaurant and eat, the bombing would start and we would have to go back down again. I was scared of the planes sending bombs. One lady was pregnant, she gave birth in the cellar. It was amazing and really sad. Poor war baby.

In some cities, whole families decided to abandon homes they had lived in for generations. But there were few buses and cars, and often the shelling didn't stop long enough for people to leave. Just as soon as the shelling would stop, people thought that they could get out. But as they stepped outside the shelling would suddenly start again without warning. So they were forced to remain in their homes.

Not only was there constant shelling in the villages, there was the additional terror of being directly attacked. The soldiers of the different ethnic factions terrorized civilian populations in order to force them to leave their homes. First the villages were shelled, forcing the people to live in shelters for days on end, unable to go out for food, or to get any news of what was happening around them. The children were terrified. When the shelling subsided, the enemy army entered and terrorized the population. Soldiers rounded up the men and either massacred them or took a large number of prisoners. Sometimes an orgy of killing would begin when soldiers who were either drunk or drugged committed atrocities. Those villagers who survived fled in terror, their villages and lives altered forever.

One young Croat who lived with his family in the village of Doljani was attacked by Muslims in July 1993. He remembers how the morning of the attack began with the barking of a dog, one that seldom barked. Later his sister saw five strange soldiers, who fired at her. The family hid together in the pantry of their house. But there was no escape.

Soldiers were banging at the door and yelling, "Open the door." Once they had broken down the door, they banged on the door of the pantry. They pulled on the door and managed to break in and fired on us. Since my sister was first, a bullet hit her in the stomach and she fell right away. They kicked her repeatedly, saying she was dead, yet they wouldn't stop beating her, even though she had died.

Serbs, more than any other group, often terrorized women and young girls by raping them, not only doing violence to their bodies, but also to their souls. Jelica, a teenager living with her family in a refugee camp, fears that this fate befell a friend of hers.

A Muslim woman and her little girl, two of some 500 Muslims and Croats being evacuated from Sarajevo to Prague, wave good-bye to loved ones as the bus pulls away.

I had a friend in Bugojno. She is now in prison. She is only sixteen. I don't know anything about her and I have no way of finding out. I am very worried because I have seen what they do to girls my age. I have horrible nightmares about soldiers raping young girls. Some of my cousins are between Travnik and Novi Travnik. It is really dangerous there, and I am so worried about them because they are girls about my age.

Ivan, a young Croat, comes from Bijelo Rojea, an ethnically mixed village in Bosnia. The Muslims and Croats wanted to push the Serbs out of his village. During that time, Ivan went with his mother and brother to Medugorje to be safe. They lived in a hotel filled with refugees. His father remained in his village to fight against the Serbs.

When the Muslim and Croat forces had successfully pushed the Serbs

"The hardest thing is knowing that there are some friends I may never see again." —Jelica (left) and her sister Monica.

Ivan playing in a cabana outside the hotel where he now lives (*facing page*).

out of the area, Ivan's mother took her two sons to the village to visit their father and check out the possibility of returning home. They arrived at the village and found everything seemingly normal. Red Cross officials told everybody to stay in the village: The situation was under control. But when the Red Cross left, the Muslims attacked the Croats in the village. They put many people in prison and in work camps.

As soon as the fighting started, Ivan's father gathered his family in the car and fled. While they were driving away, a grenade fell very close to their car. Ivan's grandparents died instantly. His mother was wounded in the head and lost consciousness. His father was severely wounded in his arm, and the car was badly damaged, but he managed to continue driving. Ivan says:

> *It's very bad what people are doing. I just wanted to visit my house. I didn't shoot at them so why did they do that. They are crazy. They can fight between themselves. They can fight the Chetniks [Serbs] but not at me. They are crazy. I don't want to go back. Maybe it's better to send someone to shoot at them.*

Ivan's mother cannot believe that such a thing has happened to them. In the village the Muslims and Croats were allies. Many of her neighbors and close friends were Muslims. Ivan's brother is still in shock. He hardly talks anymore. Both boys wake up at night screaming. She tries to explain

things to them. But how can she when she herself doesn't understand the events? The boys are always asking her: "What happened to Grandma? What happened to Grandpa?" She doesn't know what to say. She doesn't know how to explain their deaths to them. Why did they die? What was the sense of their deaths? She really doesn't know. Her children use ethnic slurs such as Chetnik [Serb] and Balija [Muslim] without knowing what they mean. They can't associate these words with the friends they used to go to school with.

Children just can't understand why they are victims of war. Sandra, age twelve, was playing at home with a friend of hers. There was some fighting around the house, and a grenade fell into the room where they were playing. Sandra's friend was killed instantly. Sandra felt something in her stomach and realized that she had been hit by shrapnel.

She has already had several operations to repair the damage and still needs several more. She has been robbed not only of her childhood but also of an essential part of her womanhood. Having children is central to the lives of women in traditional countries, but because of her injuries Sandra will not be able to bear children. So she will always feel unfulfilled. She cannot understand why, because adults want to make war, she has to suffer so deeply.

In Bosnia's war, everyone is a potential target, a seven-year-old child is just as much a target as a thirty-five-year-old soldier. Editha, eight years old, has been in the hospital for several weeks. The hospitals try to keep

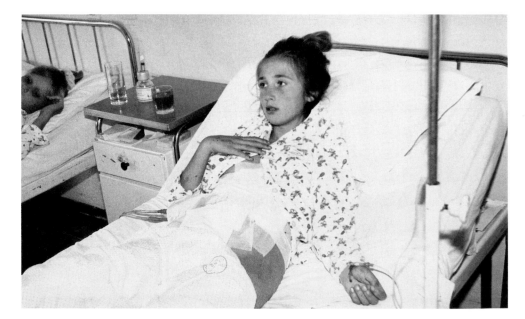

Sandra's whole future has been changed by her war injuries.

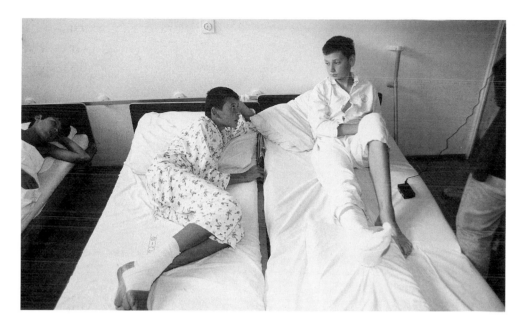

Children are kept in hospitals for as long as possible to keep them safe.

children as long as possible because it is safer for them there. Editha describes being shot by a sniper in Sarajevo:

I saw his face. He was looking straight at me. Then he lifted his gun and shot me. The bullet hit me in the leg. Why did he want to shoot at me? I didn't do anything wrong. I really don't understand.

What Editha cannot understand is why he shot her on purpose. The fact that children are intentional targets in a war makes them lose their faith in adults as providers and protectors. They suddenly realize that their parents are unable to protect them from all harm.

Some families tried to protect their children by fleeing their homes. Hundreds of thousands of people fled or were forced from their villages, leaving most of their possessions behind. They had to march through war zones and cross front lines to reach safety. More than 3 million people left their homes because of the fighting. Many walked for miles until somebody from their side found them and took them to an organized refugee camp. Often it took several months before they were able to settle somewhere.

Flight was often a nightmare. Ifeta Bjelonja and her three children walked for twenty days, sleeping in caves or in the woods, until they reached the airport outside Sarajevo. When they reached the city, they were shot at by snipers. Her son Lamer remembers:

Schools are now shelters.

We started running across the airport runway and the snipers were firing at us. I was running like crazy and I kept falling in the mud. I was running like a rabbit—running, running, running.

He and his family made it. Others didn't. Hanifo Kapa tried to leave with her husband and children. They were stopped by three Serbian soldiers, who took everybody to the schoolhouse and then separated the men from the women and children. Mrs. Kapa, her younger son, and her four daughters were told to start walking toward town. The soldiers kept her husband and her other son, twenty-two. They were bleeding when she last saw them. She believes they are dead.

A twelve-year-old boy remembers running as fast he could from soldiers. A friend was with him. Just as they reached the top of a hill, his friend was hit. The boy pulled him to an abandoned house but, seeing that there was nothing he could do for his friend, he left. Now he is depressed and feels guilty for not having saved his friend, although there was nothing he could have done.

The separation of families is one of the most painful experiences of the war. Sixty thousand children have been sent to live in other countries. Others have been sent to refugee camps or orphanages. Some were so young they cannot remember their parents or even their own names. Others mourn the loss of parents they may never see again. Anton lives in a refugee camp in Capljina with his mother. Before coming to Capljina he and his family had spent several months living in a shelter under heavy shelling. He says:

> *I miss everything about my home. I miss all my things. I miss my friends. I even miss school. But more than anything I wish my father was here.*

His mother is very worried about Anton because he is always very quiet. He never talks to anyone and he often wakes up at night screaming from terrible nightmares.

Many of the children who were sent to orphanages are not sure if their parents are dead or alive. Many have witnessed killings and torture. They suffer from nightmares and receive little therapy. As time passes, they begin to lose the will to live. Some do not even take basic precautions when danger from gunfire is near. They act as if they expect to be killed. Others panic at the slightest noise. A clicking toy becomes, in their mind, the sound of a hand grenade.

A little boy prays near his father's grave.

Children miss their homes almost as much as they miss their parents. Slavko, who was driven out of his home says,

> *Everybody needs to have a home. Everybody needs a place where they are born and where they grow up. I can't explain how important it is to have a home. Everybody has to have one.*

It's hard for any child to leave his or her home and belongings. But for war refugees, everything that represents security suddenly is taken from them. They have lost not just their house, toys, and clothes but also their fathers, mothers, aunts, uncles, and friends. There is little joy in their lives.

Jelica, the teenager who fears that her friends have been raped, is just becoming aware of how she looks and is starting to notice boys. She can no longer take her time making herself look pretty. She can't spend hours talking to her friends about boys. She has no privacy, no special time with her mother to share all the changes she's going through. Now everybody is occupied with survival, making sure there is enough food and fuel for heat.

> *I miss freedom. I want to be free to go and come as I please. I miss my friends. The hardest thing is knowing that there are some friends I might never see again. I miss peace. And I miss my home. Here we don't have enough things. It would be better if we had all our things. But anyway there is nothing to do. We are just here, waiting.*

The school at Siroki Brijeg, where Jelica now lives, is very old. It has been turned into a refugee camp. The building is run-down. The concrete floors look permanently wet. The paint is peeling, and the whole place smells musty. There is a grille all around the staircase that makes the place look like a prison. Many families now live in what used to be the classrooms. These rooms are medium-sized and have wooden planks on the floor to give a semblance of warmth. Twelve bunk beds are lined up against the walls. Two large tables are used for cooking and eating. The bathrooms are communal. There are no showers, only sinks. There is no privacy of any kind. Several families live in each classroom, and they must sleep, eat, dress, and wash in front of everybody else. Almost all refugee camps in Bosnia fit this description.

The younger children run around the village or hang out in the hallways. They have very little to keep them busy. Their mothers are occupied cleaning, cooking, and creating a home out of the mess the war has put them in. The children welcome visitors, shouting and screaming, excited to see new faces. They offer to show them around, to take them wherever they want to go. The children will do anything to relieve the endless days of waiting.

Zoran is thirteen years old. After fleeing their village, his family was placed in a refugee camp in an old school. They have been there for eight months.

The refugee camp is really boring. There is nothing to do. Sometimes we play ball, but there is only one and we have to share it with everybody. I really miss my sheep. I had trained her to do tricks. I played with her all the time. But I had to leave her at home when we left. I don't know if she is still alive. I'm afraid that somebody ate her.

Jelica is deeply hurt and angry by what has happened to her and her family. She can never understand how people can be so cruel to each other. The loss of her home has made her feel deeply insecure. Like Zlata, she tries to distance herself from her emotional pain by keeping a journal.

Living in only one room.

I keep a journal now. When I write I can forget all that has happened to me. It helps me to stop thinking of the past. It makes me feel a little better. But I have lost hope of ever going back home. We have been here for almost two months and nothing has changed.

Children who were forced to leave their homes, whose whole lives have been turned upside down, find it very hard to see a way out. When they first came to the refugee camps they were sure that they would go back home very soon. But as the months become years, they lose hope of ever seeing their homes and villages again. They lose faith in their own futures. Admin, sixteen years old, has been in a refugee camp for over a year now. His family was separated as they fled Sarajevo through the mountain pass at Mount Igman.

I am depressed. I don't want to see any more war. There is no future. There is no longer any hope. There is nothing for me now. Things here won't be solved for another twenty years. I just want to find a way for going abroad.

The war creates confusion in the minds of children. Villages that were once ethnically mixed suddenly found themselves ethnically divided. One day Croats, Serbs, and Muslims lived together. The next, the Muslims and Croats attacked one another. That once they were friends, neighbors, schoolteachers, even family members was completely forgotten. It is shocking for people living in peace to suddenly find themselves attacked by former friends. Their sense of betrayal is very deep. For children, like Admin, the war is even harder to understand, and the sense of betrayal goes even deeper. Jelica, a Croat, says:

I can't describe to you the pain that I feel because of what is happening. I will never forget and I will never forgive. I hate the Muslims. I will never be able to live with them again. I had Muslim friends before the war started but once the fighting broke out it was finished.

When a friend becomes an enemy children are so deeply hurt by such a betrayal that their whole world is shaken. They cannot forgive the factions that caused such pain, even if it means that they must turn their backs on their friends.

Marja Vrhovac, a nine-year-old from Travnik, is very disturbed by what she has seen and been through.

I have a very bad feeling about this war. I am very angry. Very angry with Croat forces. I am not at all sorry about Croat refugees. I am very angry because they pushed me from my home.

Sandra, the girl who was seriously wounded by a grenade, also feels great anger.

I want to kill the people who are making this war. They are not people, they are not even animals. They are worse than animals. I just want this war to end and for me to be OK again. I was waiting so long for this war to end, but now I have lost hope. Maybe deep inside I still hope that the war will end soon. I am glad that there are no wars like here anywhere else in the world. I am so angry. I don't have anything left for me. I have stopped dreaming of the future. I never expected this to happen to me. I am waiting for God to help me. I am waiting for someone to help me.

Making their own fun *(top left)*.

In the camps at Siroki Brijeg, children spend their long days worrying about the future.

Like this eight year old, too many children have lost their lives since the beginning of the civil war in the former Yugoslavia.

But Zlata, despite the fact that she is a Muslim victim of Serbian brutality, is not deceived by ethnic hatred. With a great deal of wisdom, she is aware of how people are being manipulated by the war. In her diary she writes:

> *Among our friends, in our family, there are Serbs, Croats and Muslims. It's a mixed group and I never knew who was a Serb, a Croat and a Muslim. Now politics has started meddling around. It has put an "S" on Serbs, an "M" on Muslim and a "C" on Croats. It wants to separate them.*

In 1994, the opening ceremony of the Winter Olympics in Lillehammer, Norway, was dedicated to peace and caring for the earth. It was a moving ceremony, especially when hundreds of white doves, eternal symbols of peace, were released. In his opening speech, the president of the Olympic Committee reminded the world that the former Olympic city of Sarajevo was still under siege. He urged the world to hold a minute of silence for Sarajevo and called on the leaders of the world to give peace a chance.

In the spring of 1994, the warring parties finally agreed to a cease-fire. But even if they are not actually shooting at each other, they are still a long way from real peace. And even if that peace comes soon, can these children, who have been so damaged by war, find a way to reclaim their lives? Many have lost their families. Even more will never see their homes again. And many if not all have lost their childhood. They have grown up too soon, seen too much suffering, and suffered too much themselves. Zlata speaks for many children when she sums up her own life.

> *That's my life. The life of an innocent eleven-year-old schoolgirl. A schoolgirl without a school, without the fun and excitement of school. A child without games, without friends, without the sun, without birds, without nature, without fruit, without chocolate, without sweets, with just a little powdered milk.*
>
> *In short, a child without a childhood. A wartime child. I and thousands of other children in this town that is being destroyed, that is crying, weeping, seeking help, but getting none. God will this ever stop, will I ever be a schoolgirl again? This stupid war is destroying my childhood. STOP THE WAR! I NEED PEACE!*

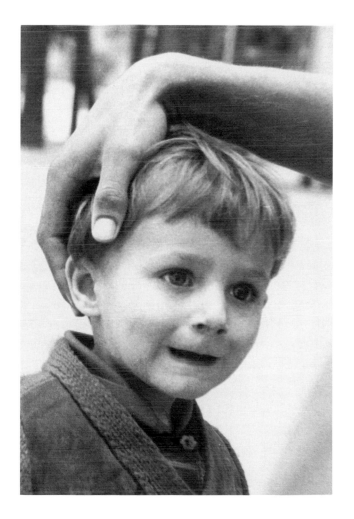

A mother's protective hand.

5

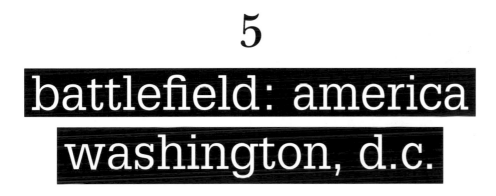

battlefield: america
washington, d.c.

A child in Sarajevo wishes he could come to America. "They don't have war there," he says. He doesn't know that there are cities in the United States where many streets are a battleground. And where children are killing children.

Washington, D.C., is one of these war zones. Children are gunned down in sight of the White House while drug dealers sell their wares on street corners. A recent report revealed that the victims of most violent crimes are children between the ages of twelve and seventeen. Some teenagers have become so violent that one politician confessed, "Let's face it, we're afraid of our children. We're scared to death of them."

In the period from 1981 to 1990, more than half of all teenage deaths were homicides committed by other teens or killings by police who caught a teenager committing a crime. Many Washington children are caught in a war over control of the drug market. Dealers, many of whom are adults, use children to sell their drugs to other children. In 1993, 1,658 minor-age children were arrested in Washington D.C. on drug charges. In one study of 400 youths, over eighty said they used or sold drugs. Ninety-two admitted to being involved with group attacks on individuals and twenty admitted they had shot, stabbed, or killed someone.

While most of the children living in Washington D.C are not involved with the drug trade, they are victimized by its presence. They find them-

A child draws an image from his life.

selves trapped in a world that is so violent and crazy that they constantly worry about their own safety and that of their friends and family. Because of the random violence, their parents fear to let them go out except for school. Yvette, who is seventeen and a high school student about to graduate, remembers her childhood.

> *I was kind of afraid to go outside because of the violence. My grandmother wouldn't let me go outside much, even to go to the store or to play with some of the kids that I was allowed to play with. She just let me go to school.*

Yvette remembers once living in a neighborhood when it wasn't like that:

> *I used to be able to at least sit on my steps and feel safe in front of my house. But now sometimes, like you're just afraid to walk out the front door and I don't know . . . It's gotten worse. At first you didn't hear any gunshots. But now you hear a lot of gunshots in the night.*

Even the best efforts to shelter children from violence can fail. Sometimes children are accidentally killed by stray bullets while watching television in their apartments. When Yvette was ten, she often stayed home after school for safety. Even that was not enough to protect her from witnessing violence.

> *I used to live over on First and K Street in a town house complex in a corner that was really closed up. One time we saw a man die right in front of our steps. We were looking out of the window and what happened was . . . a lot of the boys just like jumped him. And they had bottles and sticks and stuff. They were just beating on him. He wasn't from our side of town. They were in the parking lot at first and he was trying to get away. He was just trying to get out of the parking lot. He was trying to walk across the parking lot and they just kept beating him. I was about ten. It was like when he reached our steps he just collapsed. My grandmother called an ambulance. When it got there, he was dead.*

Even schools, once considered neutral ground, have become part of the battlefield. Schools are supposed to be havens where children feel safe and have time to learn. But some schools today are so violent that students are afraid to go to them. Tameka, age ten, is one of them:

Schoolyard warnings.

"Disneyland is the safest place I have ever been to." —Tameka (right)

I get mad about the violence. At my school there are always shootings, so we sometimes have to lay on the ground. So we don't go to the playground that much. The worst thing about this place is that you could just be looking at someone and he can say "what are you looking at!" and shoot you just like that. It's crazy. Disneyland is the safest place I have ever been to. I would love to live there.

Reggie is fourteen and lives in an apartment complex with his mother. His father abandoned them, and he hasn't seen or spoken to him in three years. Having seen violence increase dramatically in his school, Reggie feels that he has to take steps to protect himself.

Once we were at school and these kids drove by and shot into the crowd. This girl got shot, she got shot in the heart and still lived. Of course I was going to get myself a gun. I was not going to let them shoot at me and do nothing about it. I can't take it to school because we have metal detectors. 'Cause there were too many guns. Three of my friends got shot. One of them was killed by a cop.

Tony is sixteen and lives with relatives. He is trying very hard to keep away from the violence around him. He feels that many students carry guns not only to protect themselves but as a status symbol.

Kids carry guns and get into trouble to be popular. If you deal drugs you have friends, you feel popular. There is so much peer pressure that it is very hard not to give into it.

Many younger children are attracted to the violence. They see older kids acting tough and often want to be like them. Tameka lives in the center of one of the most crime-ridden areas in Washington. She sees how younger children get drawn into the world of violence every day.

A gun is the way for many D.C. children to feel respected or powerful *(facing page).*

Across the street from my school there is a junior high school called Shaw, and when the big guys from Shaw come to our playground, some kids who have older brothers there hang out with them, 'cause they think its cool. So they wind up being shot or killed 'cause they hang out with the wrong crowd. I fight if I have to but I wouldn't take a gun, 'cause I want to live in peace. My mama says that if you live around a gun you die.

Parents fear what their children might learn on the streets *(right)*.

Young men join gangs to gain respect and a sense of family.

The goal of many teenage boys is to become a member of a gang. Joining serves two purposes. The gang provides a form of family life, offering friendship and support. Often it substitutes for the family that its members never had. Many boys see the gang as providing the only chance they have to earn a living, even if that living is earned illegally. Some feel that the gang is their only means of protection in a violence-filled world. In return, the gang requires one thing from its members—loyalty. Many youngsters, like Hard Rock, say they are ready to die for their fellow gang members. They are also ready to steal, fight, and kill if necessary. For violence is the ultimate test of a gang member: The more violent he is, the more he is respected and admired. Hard Rock, who is now in a special school, remembers his days as a gang member:

I was part of a gang, I did a whole lot of dirt. I beat people up, I shot at people. I did a lot of things. The first time I got in a fight I was in junior high. I beat up on some kid and it gave me a real adrenaline rush. I didn't want to box. I wanted to fight and kill. After that I started needing money, so I started robbing people. I was thirteen and I needed money for everyday needs, clothes, food. I was taking care of myself at the time; my father was incarcerated and my mother was intoxicated. I got to stay in the gang 'cause I live around here. I can go home and someone might want to shoot me. . . . A gang is about being with your friends.

The basic law of the gang is respect. This is one reason gang members carry guns. They feel that a gun automatically earns respect for its carrier. It gives him the power of life and death over another individual. And once a boy carries a gun, he may be called upon to use it. For it is an unwritten law in many gangs that the punishment for disrespecting a gang member is death. When members of rival gangs disrespect each other, the result can be a battle. Reggie has been in many fights over inter-gang insults:

Sometimes one of the kids from the street up the road provokes one of us. So we get together and respond. They have guns so we have guns. And when we get into a fight, usually we are more than twenty on each side.

The codes of respect and disrespect are very subtle. A young person can get killed without ever knowing what he did to offend someone else. Young people in Washington, D.C., live in a world in which they are shot

Fashion is very important
to inner-city children:
Many kids are willing to
kill over a pair of Nikes or
a college jacket.

for the way they look at someone, the street they live on, the school they
go to, the clothes they wear, or the girlfriends they have—or just for being
in the wrong place at the wrong time. One former gang member in another city once explained the extremes to which some teenagers in his
gang carried the concept of respect:

> *When someone steps on your shoes, you kill him. Don't matter it's an acci-*
> *dent. Don't matter he says, " 'scuse me." All that matters is that he stepped*
> *on your shoes and nothin' can 'scuse that. He gotta die.*

Yet behind the feeling of pride in belonging to a gang is often a feeling of despair and emptiness. Lepricon, fourteen, is a member of a girl
gang. She has been arrested several times on a number of charges, including assault. She lives with her mother and is completely disillusioned with
life. She knows that she is on the road to jail, but it doesn't seem to bother
her. The only things that seem to matter are her friends and the streets.
Being arrested brands you as bad, and on the streets, bad is good. Lepricon has no plans for the future:

> *Dreams? Who has dreams? Don't you know that dreams never come true. I*
> *don't care about what is going to happen to me. I have dropped out of*
> *school, but since I was arrested the judge is forcing me to go back. I have a*
> *curfew too, but I don't care. I am not going to be home by eight P.M. No way.*

Children like Lepricon find it difficult to believe in anything, including themselves. They do not value anything. It is easy for them to break the law and disobey an authority that they don't respect. Like many despairing teenagers, Lepricon is a drug user and says she is proud of it.

Contrary to the impression sometimes given by the news media, most teenagers do not join gangs. Many keep clear of drugs and violence, although they are often pressured by gang members to join. It takes strength of character to keep away from violence and drugs and to keep a straight head, especially when you may be attacked and humiliated. But many feel it is worth the risk because they want to build a good future for themselves. Donnell, who is seventeen, was wounded during a drive-by shooting. The bullet did no serious damage. Donnell has chosen not to take revenge.

On the street, friends are what matter most.

To buy candy, children have to go into liquor stores where owners stand behind bulletproof glass.

After I was shot at I was tempted to get a gun to protect myself, but I came to the conclusion that another gun would just take another life. I think that anyone that is in a gang or has a gun needs attention and is basically insecure. It has a lot to do with family background. If you pray, you don't need a gun for security.

Security is the key to the problem of gangs. Many inner-city children feel that the world has forgotten them. They don't feel they are part of America. They feel they cannot trust adults. They cannot trust their own parents and brothers and sisters. This feeling of mistrust makes them feel lonely, alienated, and lost—like nine-year-old Jason, who loves animals and keeps out of trouble. Jason hates his older brother, who is a crack dealer and constantly abuses him. More than once Jason has called the police on him, which was dangerous to do. He says they didn't come because "they don't like to come here 'cause they don't give a damn about us." He feels the system has let him down. Many children feel that the police are indifferent to their problems. And worse than indifferent: They believe the police are prejudiced and refuse to enter their neighborhoods because they don't care. When the police do arrive, youngsters feel that they are often arrested for no reason. Reggie recalls:

I got arrested because my friend held up this guy on the street. I was on the other sidewalk, so the cop thought I was looking out for him. So he arrested me.

The feeling of police hostility against them, the sense of isolation produced by living in "violent ghettos," and their lack of a stable family life make it difficult for such children to understand why they should stay out of trouble. Smiley feels that his situation is hopeless, no matter what he accomplishes.

My parents died. My dad killed my mom and ever since then I have been living with a relative. My relative died, so now I live with a friend. Every time I try to do good nothing happens. I try to be good but I don't get anything out of it. I just work, get bored, and nothing changes. I graduated from high school, I didn't drop out. I was involved in so many school activities. I was a cheerleader, I was on the wrestling team, I was in school plays. And I didn't get nothing out of being good.

Often a young boy becomes a father before he reaches manhood.

Babies having babies *(facing page)*.

A child's chances for success usually depend on having a stable family and community life. But communities like Washington are all too often left to solve their problems with limited means and with little assistance. Many parents, with problems of their own, are not able to be good parents. Young women often become mothers while barely into their teens—"babies having babies." Many mothers have too many children to care for without support. In Washington, D.C., 55 percent of all children live in single-parent households, usually with their mother or grandmother. Some live with friends or on the streets. Unstable families and the lack of economic security (one child in four lives below the poverty line, a level of income below which one is classified as "poor" according to government standards), makes Washington the worst American city for a child to live in today. Boys often grow up without their fathers, so they lack a good male role model. Many teens stray from home, fending for themselves on the violent streets of the city. Many, like Reggie, miss their fathers and yearn to be loved and cared for properly. He says, "I love my dad. I miss him and I wish he could be here with me to give me advice."

Some parents, realizing that they have failed their children, have tried to make amends. Joan, a former addict who admits she neglected her children for the sake of drugs, is now forty years old and a grandmother.

Many Washington, D.C., schools body search student's before they enter the school grounds.

I am enrolled in a literacy program and I am trying to better my life for the sake of my grandchildren. I am clean now, and I am trying to make a big effort. The father of my children is in jail for dealing drugs. It is really tough to live around here.

If children have good relationships with their parents, make the right friends, and receive the necessary support at home, they usually turn out well. Some families are joining community groups and encouraging young people to go to church or to a mosque instead of hanging out on the streets. Donnell, the seventeen-year-old who decided not to take revenge after being shot, is a student at Duke Ellington School for the Arts.

My family always kept me in the church. The majority of my friends have church backgrounds, and the ones that don't have very strict parents. Their main focus is to go to school, be home before dark, get their homework done, set their priorities straight.

NEW RULES

* Respect Yourself.
* Respect Each Other.
* Share.
* Take Your Turn.
* Help Each Other to learn, not to com-pete.
* Help The Ones Who Don't know The Games
* Set Good Examples
* NO Dangerous Games.
* NO Weapons.
* NO DRUGS.
* NO Alcohol.
* NO Smoking.
* NO Fighting.
* NO Stealing.
* NO Destroying Property.
* NO Gambling.
* NO Beepers.
* NO Littering.
* Must wear T-Shirts.
* Do not Use Strong Words Against One another.

NUEVAS REGLAS

The basic rules at the Latin American Youth Center, where teenagers go after school *(above)*.

Some religious santuaries are isolated havens in a dangerous community.

Some inner-city children try to rationalize the violent world in which they live. They view their surroundings as a learning experience about the real world. They regard people who live in safer areas as living in fantasyland. Tanya believes that violence is a part of life, and a reality for which every youngster should be prepared.

I wouldn't like to live in a safe place because it is boring, nothing happens. And plus if one day I am forced to move away from that safe place, I would like to know how to handle myself in dangerous situations. If you live in a safe place you never learn about the real world.

Efforts are being made in Washington to rescue children from the violence. The task is difficult. Seventy-five percent of youths released from detention centers are likely to commit new crimes. While in custody, many resolve to change their lives. But once the children are back on the street, the pressures often overwhelm them. If they were hanging out with a gang or dealing in drugs, they are immediately challenged to resume the old life. Intensive therapy sometimes helps, but it takes months or sometimes years to change. Poor children's anger is deep, and many are reluctant to give it up. Hard Rock, a former gang member who is doing well in a special school, frankly admits that he has not completely given up his old ways.

When I came here I was still hustling, but then I stopped because of this place and also because I got arrested. This school I am in now is allowing me to do what I have always wanted to do, which is draw and paint. If I go to another school and I witness violence it makes me want to be part of the violence. If one of my gang gets in a fight I am going to fight too.

Most children who live in inner cities never fully recover from the pain they have experienced. Without psychological help, they will feel despair all their lives. They have seen things children should never see. Death hangs over their lives like a plague. They don't care whether they live or die. They are resigned to whatever happens, a feeling that haunts Tony at times:

I don't care. I am going to die one day anyway. So I don't really care. What difference does it make if I die now or later? It is exactly the same thing.

Not everybody in inner
cities subscribes to the
glorification of violence.

Many young people have already planned their funerals and willed
their prom dresses to their friends because they do not believe that they
will live long. Lucky says she does not think about the future.

*I think about today. You have to take life one day at a time. There is no
reason one should plan for the future, because there might be no future.*

Others, however, do manage to overcome despair. They dream of the
day when the war on the streets will end and they will be able to play
outdoors and go to school without worrying about being killed. They
dream of eating when they are hungry and having a nice home and their
own family. Smiley, although she is a gang member, still dreams of a normal life.

*I would love to have kids. If I have a kid I will spoil him rotten. But I will
also teach him how to fight, because in this world you always have to watch
your back. I would give my kid everything that I didn't get because I didn't
have any parents.*

Too many inner-city children are killed before reaching their teens.

Family grieving at the funeral of their son, a victim of street violence.

Hard Rock, despite his years with a gang, is in his last year of school at Duke Ellington High School. He plans to go to college in New York, make a life for himself, and contribute something to his neighborhood.

If I survive, my wish is to have money, 'cause you see money takes care of a lot of things—clothes, food, schools. You don't have to worry about nothing really. If you don't have no money you get depressed. If you get depressed, you want to get money. When you can't get money, you want to get money. When you can't take money, you kill to take money. If I make it, I will always come back here and try to help as much as I can.

Tony lives with friends of his family because he doesn't get along with his mother's boyfriend. He moved to a different neighborhood because he didn't want to get in his mother's way. He misses his mother and grandmother very much and hopes he can live with them again very soon. Even though Tony can be pessimistic, he has days when he feels good about himself. He says that he used to be wild but now he has "come down" a lot because he is "not ready to die yet." He is active in a community group and keeps himself out of trouble.

I used to get into a lot of trouble, but now it is over. I try to be as good as I can. I want to join the military in order to be able to go to college because that is the only way I can afford tuition.

Despite the fact that Reggie has been involved with gangs, he still dreams of a hopeful future. He wishes that the violence could end and that there was no such thing as a gun. He fantasizes about being a basketball player. But whatever he does, he says his strongest wish "is to live to be real old."

Are these young people's dreams realistic? It depends upon how strongly motivated they are to change their lives. Some children growing up in the inner cities do manage to make constructive lives for themselves. However, without outside help an increasing number fall by the wayside. It is a race against time, a race that cannot be won without help. For while Washington, D.C., is one of the richest cities in the country, it is one of the most dangerous places in the world for a young person to

Kids pursue their dream on this makeshift court.

Drug dealers work just blocks from the Capitol.

grow up. In its own way, Washington, a city that symbolizes the best of America in so many ways, is as much a battlefield as Mozambique, Beirut, and El Salvador once were. For them, the fighting has stopped. Even in Sarajevo, cease fires give hope that an end to the fighting is in sight. In Washington, though, the war goes on day after day.

Graffiti eulogy.

index